Read '90

A
Harlequin
Romance

OTHER

Harlequin Romances

by NERINA HILLIARD

557—NURSE CAROL'S SECRET
(Originally published under the title "The Time is Short")
840—THE HOUSE OF ADRIANO
927—THE SCARS SHALL FADE
1302—TEACHERS MUST LEARN

DARK STAR

by

NERINA HILLIARD

HARLEQUIN BOOKS

TORONTO
WINNIPEG

First published in 1968 by Mills & Boon Limited,
London, England.

SBN 373-01268-3

Harlequin Canadian edition published January, 1969
Harlequin U.S. edition published April, 1969

Reprinted 1973

All the characters in this book have no existence outside the imagination of the Author, and have no relation whatsoever to anyone bearing the same name or names. They are not even distantly inspired by any individual known or unknown to the Author, and all the incidents are pure invention.

Printed in Canada

1268

CHAPTER 1

THE door was not slammed, but it was nevertheless closed with a decisive snap, the sound a door makes when someone who would dearly love to swing it vigorously behind them is restrained by an overriding caution.

Leigh glanced up with a faint smile on her lips as a bundle of papers was dumped unceremoniously on her desk by a redhead whose temper was quite obviously approaching boiling point, and she enquired with a note of sympathy in her voice as she recognised the danger signals in the other girl's green eyes:

"Anything wrong? You seem slightly disturbed."

"Disturbed?" Miss Kerrigan made a helpless gesture, as if it was beyond her to describe precisely what was wrong. "One day I'll tell that man just what I think of him . . . and you can take it from me it will be far from polite!"

Leigh Dermot's lips twitched a little, and a gleam of amusement appeared in her eyes. They were darkly blue eyes that fascinated most people, and anyone taking a further look at her would have been equally fascinated by the pale creaminess of her skin and the neatly braided hair that was arranged in a coronet about her small finely shaped head. She looked deceptively serene and deceptively cool and composed, despite the fact that her hair was a pale flame that deepened into living fire when a light played over it or the right sort of background threw it into prominence; and although most people thought her a cool and controlled young woman the warmth and the humour that dwelt in the curves of her shapely mouth should have given them the lie direct.

Anyone who took the trouble to study her deliberately would have suspected in time an ardent disposition rather than one that was content to allow life to drift idly past her . . . and they could so easily have been right.

Kerry Kerrigan—christened, in actual fact, Rosalyn Kerrigan, but almost always known by her nickname of Kerry—knew her very well, and she had no doubts at all about the qualities that resided beneath the matt perfection of her magnolia-pale skin. She knew also that at the moment Leigh was not taking her seriously.

"Oh, well," she said, as she seated herself on a corner of the desk, "perhaps it would be a bit difficult to find the courage. That boss of ours may be attractive, but he's the most intimidating example of his sex I've met so far."

"The trouble with you," Leigh told her, "is that you allow him to make you jittery."

"Jittery?" That brought the fire back to the green eyes. "I was getting plain mad with him just now, and I simply don't understand how you've managed to stick him for three years. "Three years!" She rolled her eyes. "You must have the patience of a plaster saint!"

Leigh shrugged almost carelessly.

"I'm merely completely indifferent to him and his moods."

"Lucky you . . . since you're the one who has to answer his bell most of the time! But there's one thing I'll say about the owner of Merediths," Kerry conceded, "and that is that he never says a word out of place."

"Never gets amorous, you mean?" Leigh's lovely lips quirked upwards at the corners. "The poor man wouldn't know how to if he tried!"

An angry buzzing like a swarm of infuriated bees let loose upon them broke into the peace of Leigh's small office, and Kerry bounced off the desk and took refuge in the general office adjoining. Leigh gathered up pencils and notebook and presented herself at the door of her employer's inner sanctum—the door that had been so nearly slammed by Kerry; but which it was inevitable she had not slammed because Ruiz Aldoret was simply not the type of man who would have permitted violence of that sort. He was not the type of man to permit anything in the nature of familiarity or contempt for his august position as Head of the House of Meredith, and to answer him back would have required a degree of strong-mindedness certainly not possessed by Kerry.

Ruiz Aldoret could quell with a quiet word and create nervous tension with a single look. He was competence itself, had a complete and absolute knowledge of the concerns of his firm and never spared himself when hard work was a necessity; and by the same token he was so ruthlessly efficient that he expected the same efficiency from everyone who served him. If they failed to justify a position with the firm he sacked them. But he never sacked them unfairly, and one glance from his cold, dark eyes made it plain that he would brook no argument. His was the final word on all occasions, and he was the final authority.

Leigh felt little or no apprehension when she entered his office, but she did glance at him secretly to discover whether his mood was particularly dangerous. He was standing behind his desk when she entered, his tall figure dominating the situation, as it were, while he rummaged impatiently through the chaos of papers on his desk. Leigh interpreted the state of the barometer as 'stormy,' and hoped it might be possible after all to avert a storm. But she was not entirely hopeful, for Ruiz Aldoret was half Spanish. Merediths had come to him from his mother's side of the family.

"You wanted me, Mr. Aldoret?"

"I would not have rung for you if I didn't want you," he snapped in answer. He was undoubtedly an attractive man, but his good looks were marred by the signs of evident temper. "Where is the Brown & Kenton contract?"

Leigh's lips compressed as she went to a cabinet against the wall and produced a bulky file of documents.

"You asked me to put it away last night," she explained.

She felt him relax slightly, but only very slightly. He took the file from her and produced the contract, read it through with frowning brows, and then glanced up to see her still standing before his desk. His black brows knitted together, and then the expression on his face became cool and smooth.

"All right, you may go."

Leigh went, stifling an absurd desire to giggle, even though she sometimes left his office feeling as if she had been put through a mincing machine.

Kerry was right, she thought, when she resumed her seat behind her own desk. Ruiz Aldoret could make you furious . . . if you allowed yourself to become furious. But fortunately she had greater control over her emotions than the fiery Kerry possessed, and in addition she was used to this form of treatment. By contrast with Ruiz Aldoret her Bruce had very nearly an angelic quality.

She allowed herself to think of Bruce, and might have fallen into a daydream but for the fact that the buzzer sounded again, but not nearly so impatiently or peremptorily as it had done before.

Ruiz Aldoret was pacing up and down his office when she entered it for the second time in a matter of minutes. He regarded her with dark, penetrating, and faintly curious eyes.

"Miss Dermot," he said, "do you know of a good restaurant not too far from the office? I have a conference with a representative of Brown & Kenton's and will not have time to go to my usual place."

Leigh thought swiftly. There were one or two cafés nearby, but nothing of the expensive, exclusive type that would suit her employer.

"There's Ricki's," she said at last, tentatively. "It's only a few minutes' walk from here. Quite a few people from the firm frequent it. The food is good, but it's not particularly smart."

"Nevertheless it will do," he replied without hesitation. "How do I get to it?"

Leigh gave him a set of directions and he thanked her in a cool, clipped voice, then dismissed her once more to her own office. On the way to her desk she looked in at the general office to enquire of Kerry whether she would be joining her for lunch.

Kerry glanced up from the labour of typing a report.

"At Ricki's?"

"Yes. I'll see you there if His Nibs doesn't detain me for anything."

She was about to slip back into her own office, but Kerry called her back.

"By the way, a telephone call came through from Stella while you were in with His Majesty a moment ago. She said she would be driving down some time tomorrow."

Instantaneous delight sparkled in Leigh's eyes. "Stella coming home?"

Kerry looked at her with a rather closed-up expression. "You adore her, don't you?"

Leigh threw her a surprised glance. "Of course." Her

smile grew soft, like the one she kept for Bruce. "We all adore her, Kerry. And we're proud of her too. I suppose it's because she's so unexpected—beautiful, talented and clever, in a quite ordinary family."

That, undoubtedly, was just what they were—an ordinary family. That was why they were so surprised to have produced someone like Stella. The dark star, they called her jokingly, but they were all proud of Stella Nordett, the great actress, and they adored Stella Dermot as one of the family.

Kerry, who guessed something of what her friend was thinking, mentally disagreed with her. There was nothing remotely ordinary about any member of the Dermot family, even if Stella was the acknowledged beauty. Tess and Tom, the irrepressible twins, teenage Julie, just due to leave technical college where she was taking a secretarial course, beautiful Stella and the deceptively cool Leigh, there was nothing plain or ordinary about any of them. Apart from all that, she completely disagreed with some of the family ideas about Stella. Oh, undoubtedly Stella was beautiful, her glossy dark hair had the gleam of a raven's wing and was quite unexpected in a family of redheads, and the features and flawless complexion of the face that was so well known to frequenters of the cinema were all that could be desired—but that was as far as she would agree with the Dermot family legend. A completely false legend. Stella was selfish and self-seeking and her character was far from being as beautiful as her body. In any case, Kerry privately considered that Leigh was the real beauty of the family. Stella's beauty was of the more obvious kind, while Leigh's was in the chiselled, cameo planes of her face, the proud, cool poise of her head with its crown of burnished hair that could look every bit as glossy as the raven sheen on Stella's exotic, rather continental chignon that had just that little difference in its set from everyone else's. More than anything else, there was a firm, deep core of sincerity in Leigh which she was quite sure was missing from Stella. The famous actress accepted all the adulation that came her way, even that from her family, as simply her due, and she gave nothing in return save a sweetly insincere smile that meant just nothing.

At least, that was what Kerry thought, but it was the last thing she would ever have admitted to Leigh.

"Did she say how long she would be staying?" Leigh asked, and Kerry shook her head.

"As a matter of fact, she hardly said half a dozen words. She was rushing off to a press conference, or something like that. She rang home, but the number was engaged, so she rang you instead, in case she had to wait a long time for the home number to become disengaged."

Leigh smiled. "That would be just like Stella. She complained once that they never leave her alone, but I suspect she really enjoys every minute of it."

Rather grimly, Kerry agreed to herself that those words of her friend were just plain, unadulterated truth. Stella Dermot was greedy for fame and attention. She had to be the centre of attraction all the time. She had to possess everything she wanted, and if what she wanted belonged to somebody else she took it from them without a qualm, without the least thought of what havoc her greedy fingers might be causing. If she did ever think about it, it was probably a subject for amusement or merely an uncaring shrug.

When Kerry had gone back to her desk and Leigh had returned to the privacy of her own office, she sat down at her typewriter to get on with the work Ruiz Aldoret had given her, but although her fingers flew efficiently over the keys she could not stop her thoughts wandering now and again.

Would Stella like Bruce? But of course she would. It was impossible not to like him, she added to herself with a little smile in her eyes.

With that she once again went back to her work, sternly controlling the desire to daydream about Bruce, a desire that had been growing steadily more pronounced over the last few months—quite understandably, since they were now engaged. In spite of all her resolution, though it was impossible not to love Bruce almost at first sight, even though nobody would have supposed it from her deceptive coolness. A misty softness came into her eyes as she thought about him.

Dear, big, clumsy Bruce! It had been quite inevitable that she should love him when he walked into her office, grinned at her and handed her a sheaf of reports for Ruiz Aldoret from the engineering side of the factory.

The family had approved on sight, too, from her gruff solicitor father, her poised, still beautiful mother, teenage Julie, right down to the irrepressible twins, who had vouched their approval in a casual "He's O.K." which was praise and more from them. They had all teased her, of course, especially Julie, who at the last school break had had ideas of wanting to work at Aldorets when her secretarial training was finished, but Kerry's opinion was that she would probably change her mind after one encounter with Meredith's illustrious owner. Still, wherever she chose to work, it would be wonderful having her home in a few days' time when the final break-up at school was due. With Stella coming home also they would be able to have a more wonderful family reunion than they had expected. It would be a real occasion, with Stella as well as Julie.

The lunch hooter broke into her wandering thoughts and she rose to her feet to pull on the neat black jacket of her slim-fitting, tailored suit. Kerry met her outside the door of her little private office which adjoined Ruiz Aldoret's own private sanctum. They walked together through the white gates of the clean, modern factory, along the road and across to an unpretentious doorway labelled "Ricki's." The interior of the restaurant was cool and spacious, with a row of little cubicles, curtained off, along one side of the room.

Ricki herself, a middle-aged woman with dark hair faintly flecked with grey, met them and led them over to one of the curtained booths.

"By the way, your sister is here," she told Leigh.

"My sister?" Leigh echoed blankly—and then the curtains of one of the booths were drawn aside and a slender teenage girl, her pale bronze hair done up in a flying pony-tail, danced out, her brown eyes dancing with mischievous laughter.

"Surprised?"

"Julie!" Leigh looked thunderstruck. "What on earth are you doing here?"

"An epidemic of measles broke out, so they sent everybody home, at least those they were sure hadn't come in contact with it. Term had more or less finished anyway." She had been at a boarding school that was renowned for its extremely good secretarial training as well as its more general courses. "When everything is safe and sound again we're going to have the proper term ending and diploma presentation, but until then—here I am," she ended gaily.

Leigh hugged her with delighted affection and then directed a glance at the suitcase that stood on the floor.

"Don't tell me you haven't even been home yet?"

Julie shook her head. "Not yet. When I had to change at the junction I worked out that I would get here just before lunchtime, so I thought I would surprise you here."

"You certainly surprised me," Leigh agreed dryly. "What about the family? Are they expecting you?"

Julie gave her another mischievous smile. "No, I was supposed to send them a telegram to say I was on my way, but I thought I'd surprise them, too." She went back into the booth with them and sank down into a chair with a happy sigh. "Now I'm home for good—and determined to get a job at Merediths."

"Still on that old idea, are you?" Leigh commented dryly.

"Oh, definitely." Julie's eyes sparkled impishly. "I've fallen really hard for that boss of yours."

"You've never met him," Leigh retorted, no whit perturbed and knowing her young sister rather well.

"Oh, but I have," Julie retorted triumphantly. "Not to speak to, of course, but I did see him. When I passed Merediths on the way here, he was just getting into a car that must have cost a fortune, so I knew by that and by the way you described him who he must be."

"So you've fallen for Ruiz Aldoret, have you, pet?" Leigh commented with a tinge of dry amusement evident in her voice. "Mind telling me why?"

Julie sighed rapturously, with a teenager's abandon. "He's so attractive, so dark and romantic. . . ."

"And about as emotional as a bit of glacier ice," Leigh informed her dampeningly. "It's about time you were over schoolgirl crushes."

"But he's wonderful! You've been working with him for three years. You must have noticed."

"She makes up her mind rather quickly, doesn't she?" Kerry commented with a chuckle.

Leigh suspected that Julie was only joking, but some uneasy little qualm made her pretend to take the matter seriously, because Julie was at an impressionable age, and although it would most certainly pass in time, she did not want Julie falling a victim to Ruiz Aldoret's dark but undoubtedly inhuman attraction.

"Ruiz Aldoret is very attractive," she agreed slowly. "I grant you that, Julie—but as a man he's the last person a girl should fall in love with."

"Why on earth should he be?" Julie demanded. "I don't think I've seen anybody quite so good-looking in years, even some of those would-be swooner types that Stella acts with."

"By the way, Stella is coming home tomorrow," Leigh said blandly—and waited for results. She was not disappointed.

"Stella coming home?" Julie almost squeaked in her excitement. "How long for?"

Leigh shrugged. "I don't know yet. I suppose Stella herself will tell us when she arrives."

There was the same smiling delight in her eyes that had been there when she first heard the news, and Kerry was suddenly afraid for her. She had a perfectly horrible little suspicion at the back of her mind that some time or the other Stella was going to hurt her sister—very badly.

"What a lovely homecoming," Julie said delightedly. Suddenly her eyes sparkled with mischief. "Maybe we should introduce her to your boss and see what effect she has on him."

"I'm divided between loyalty and admiration of Stella and a quite horrible suspicion that he would look right through her. He might be half Spanish, but I'm quite sure he considers that women—as women—are necessary evils to be tolerated only for the survival of the race. If there was a scientific foundation dedicated to finding a way to do without women, I'm sure he would subscribe a goodly portion of the profits of Merediths to it."

Julie chuckled, but followed it almost immediately with a mock wail of dismay. "But he can't possibly think like that—not with the sort of eyes he's got!"

At about that moment the man in the next booth, completely screened off by the wooden partition, found himself quite unashamedly listening with a peculiar mixture of annoyance and irritation, even though he had heard nothing at all uncomplimentary to himself as a man. Quite obviously they did not have the slightest idea he was there, and his secretary had apparently forgotten that he also had intended to lunch at Ricki's. His car was parked around in a back lane, so that would not have reminded her, and he had already arrived and been cloistered in his own booth when Julie in turn arrived, so she would not have been able to warn them. Again quite obviously, or she would not have been talking like that herself.

At first he had felt the embarrassment of the unintentional eavesdropper, and tried not to listen; but it had been quite unavoidable, as the booths were not closed in at the top. Now something made him listen for every word, and those that followed were just as thought-provoking as the others had been.

"This is certainly a morning of surprises," Leigh's voice said dryly, but it bore little resemblance to the cool, remote voice he was accustomed to hearing from her. "Tell me about his eyes, my child. The only thing I've ever noticed is that they have a remarkable aptitude for making His Lordship's displeasure felt."

"But you must have noticed," Julie retorted, in some mystification at her sister's apparent shortsightedness. "I only had a brief glimpse of him—but you've been working for him for ages. I don't see how you could possibly have escaped falling in love with him."

"I wouldn't have dared to," Leigh countered. She recognised the dancing, teasing light in her sister's eyes and knew quite well that Julie was very far from being serious, but she decided to keep on with what she had started. On no account, if she came to work at Merediths, must Julie get a mistaken impression of the attractive owner. She was just at the romantic, impressionable age and those joking words might become serious.

"I thought too much of my career to be even remotely interested in him," she told Julie, "and when I came to know him a little better, I realised it was just as well that I hadn't conceived any romantic notions about him. He's a very good boss," she went on—for which the unsuspected listener in the next booth accorded her a mental and rather sardonic word of thanks, "if you can stand his moods," she added, thereby tempering the mental thanks she was receiving. "However, I confess I can't agree that he's in the least romantic." She ticked off his obvious good points on her fingers, dampeningly disposing of each of them in turn. "Tall and slim—nothing unusual about that. Very dark. Nothing unusual again. The majority of men with latin blood are dark—and as for being romantic—!" She laughed again, dispelling the final illusion, if Julie still harboured any. "I'm sorry to disappoint you, my child, but there's more romance in the leg of the chair on which you're at the moment sitting than in the whole of our esteemed boss. He wouldn't know how to make love to a girl if he tried."

Kerry chuckled impishly. "I'd like to see his face if he heard you say that!"

"Heaven forbid!" Then Leigh smiled. "He'd probably take it as some sort of odd compliment."

"Oh, would he!" muttered the occupant of the next booth.

"Women have no place in Ruiz Aldoret's life beyond being useful appendages for holding pencils and such like, to take down letters and attend to other clerical duties of the firm."

Even Julie laughed at that, abandoning her teasing, and then there was a lull in the conversation as the fragrant, steaming food they had ordered arrived.

After a long silence, Julie's voice came again. "Leigh, do me a favour?"

"Depends on what it is," Leigh returned warily, knowing her young sister well.

Julie chuckled. "When you get back to the office, have a good look at Ruiz Aldoret and tell me tonight if you still don't think he's good-looking."

"Whatever for?"

"Oh, just reasons."

Leigh shrugged. "I never said he wasn't good-looking... just that he's more or less a woman-hater and . . ."

"And more romance in a leg of a chair," Julie finished for her.

Leigh distrusted the dancing mischief in her sister's eyes, but did not say anything else on the subject of Ruiz Aldoret.

Shortly afterwards the man in the next booth rose to his feet, paid his bill and left, still without them suspecting that he had even been there; but on the way back to his office, although his mind was, as usual, concerned mainly with impersonal things, he could not quite forget that cool, analytical voice picking his appearance to pieces, demonstrating very clearly that she was no believer in the secretary-boss romance.

He had a successful afternoon, the Brown and Kenton contract was signed and he settled down to the rest of his work, forgetting the revealing conversation he had overheard—until his secretary came into his office to do some filing and then, quite involuntarily, he found himself watching her as she moved silently over the carpeted floor.

She was so much the expressionless and perfect secretary he was used to that he almost became convinced he had imagined that conversation, even though it was certainly her voice he had overheard. He was surprised to even find himself wondering what her ultimate decision would be if she did as her sister had asked, but although he watched her closely, neither her face nor her eyes gave away anything of what she was thinking. For all the interest she had in him personally, he might have been just another piece of furniture—which of course was just as he wanted it. No other type of secretary would have suited him.

Watching her as she moved quietly, with cool, poised grace, about his office, he found himself idly speculating whether she ever felt any real emotion. She seemed too controlled to experience anything like those hot passions which could tear human beings apart.

Leigh turned from the last of the filing cabinets, glanced down at her watch, then up at him again.

"It's almost five o'clock. Will you be wanting me any more tonight?"

"No. Goodnight."

"Goodnight, Mr. Aldoret," she answered quietly, and went out, closing the door behind her with the same quiet control that seemed to characterise all her actions.

A few minutes later, in the outer office, there was a general flurry of typewriter covers as the buzzer went, and in a few seconds the place was empty, dark—with the exception of the one light that still burned in Ruiz Aldoret's office. For hours he remained there alone, his dark, intent eyes on the papers in front of him, and then at last even he rose to his feet, locked the papers in one of the filing cabinets and pressed down a switch on the inter-office telephone.

"All right, Jennings, you can come and lock up now."

As he passed through the large main gates the night watchman saluted him respectfully, watching as the sleek, powerful car purred away into the darkness, its driver knowing that the evening before him would be exactly the same as the night before.

He would go home—although the place where he lived was never really that in his thoughts. There was only one place that was home to him and always would be. One place he could never return to. The flat he occupied, luxurious though it was, could never take the place of the white, spreading building he remembered too well, even though it had been years since he saw it last. At the mere thought of it, his hands clenched on the wheel until the knuckles stood out white—as white as the gleaming walls of Carastrano.

Then his hands relaxed their grip and he forced his mind to stop remembering so vividly. The car purred on smoothly, taking him towards the luxury flat and the elderly married couple who cared for it. They were as correct and impersonal as the rest of his life, yet sometimes he felt the hard, cold shell crack slightly and the loneliness would creep through, so that he had to clench his memory, as he had clenched his fists, until it was gone again.

Anything could cause it, but some things more than others—the tropical, feathery fronds of a palm in some travel poster, or perhaps the gleam of sunlight off some white building—but most of all it was the music. When he heard the languorous sweetness of some song or dance of old Spain, with the insistent rhythm that could tug at the senses beneath its soft appeal, then the memories would come back stronger than ever.

But he would grip those memories with the cold hardness he had bred in himself and send them far back in his mind until they meant nothing any more . . . almost.

Perhaps in a way he did deserve that analysis his secretary had given of him, over the years he had deliberately made himself fit into such a pattern—but just at that moment the memory of her cool, distant voice rankled in some strange fashion.

When Leigh arrived home that evening the furore over Julie's unexpected homecoming and the excitement caused by the prospect of Stella's visit was still going on, although beginning to settle somewhat.

Margaret Dermot, who was still attractive and even had a little of Julie's roguishness, her neat coronet of hair the same glorious shade of titian as Leigh's, with not a single grey hair in it, met her eldest daughter at the door, with an arm about Julie.

"What do you think of this cheeky brat turning up like a truant schoolgirl?" she greeted Leigh.

"Truant schoolgirl?" Julie protested. "I'm sixteen now."

"Such a great age," her mother mocked affectionately—and then the twins erupted around the side of the house and into the hallway.

There was no other way to describe it. The twins never entered anywhere—they always erupted into it and always together, like the two halves of a somewhat unpredictable whirlwind. Their hair also was in the red colour band, but an unashamed and unabashed carrots. Julie was fair, palely copper-blonde—really a most unusual and beautiful colour—her mother and eldest sister both wearing titian braids and, of course, Kerry, a constant visitor at the house, was also in the same colour band. They always said at Merediths that one of the reasons why Kerry Kerrigan had become part of the Dermot household was because she also was a redhead. All in that colour band stuck together.

The twins came to a standstill and looked up at Julie... two freckled, snub-nosed faces.

"Oh, you're home, are you?" Tom commented, delightfully casual, then nodded at his twin. "Come on, or we'll be late."

"Hi, see you later," Tess briefly greeted her newly returned sister and then vanished after her twin.

"Well!" Julie stood with hands on hips in mock indignation. Then she grinned. "The brats haven't changed one little bit."

"I doubt if they ever will," her mother laughed. She turned to Leigh as she closed the front door. "How was work today?"

Leigh shrugged. "Much the same as it always is." Her expression altered. "Isn't it wonderful about Stella coming home?"

"Too wonderful for words," her mother agreed.

Their father, a well-known and respected solicitor, came home with a briefcase full of papers, raised expressive eyebrows at the sight of Julie, seemed slightly stunned at the news that Stella was coming home, and agreed, a little dryly, that in honour of Julie's homecoming and Stella's projected arrival the following day, he certainly could not settle down to such a mundane thing as work—even if it did pay the household bills.

CHAPTER 2

STELLA arrived at the house at about eight o'clock the following evening, driving herself in a rakish sapphire blue roadster that looked as expensive and well turned out as she was.

At first sight of her sister, only a year younger than herself, Leigh felt the breath catch in her throat, as it always did. She glanced at her mother and guessed by Margaret's expression that the elder woman was experiencing the same sensations. It always happened when they looked at Stella, whether it was in person or on the screen. The girl was so absolutely perfect.

"Stella darling!" Margaret Dermot whispered, and put her arms about her exquisite actress daughter. Her lips touched the petal-soft cheek and a tantalising whiff of some expensive perfume caused her to wrinkle her nose in appreciation, then Stella had drawn herself free and was looking down at Julie with rather baffling amusement.

"Good heavens, is this little Julie?"

"Little?" Julie protested. "I happen to be sixteen now and a fully qualified junior stenographer!"

"I've told her that if she thinks that, she'd better not let Ruiz Aldoret ever see any of her work," Leigh said jokingly. She had to speak lightly, because this homecoming meant so much to all of them. She might have choked on emotion otherwise.

The thin, perfect eyebrows went up questioningly. "Ruiz Aldoret?"

"Leigh's boss," Julie informed her, and Stella looked over at her elder sister.

"Are you still working for that dreadful old martinet?"

"He's neither old nor dreadful," Julie said. "Though he does sound a bit of a martinet." She smiled impishly at her famous sister. "We thought perhaps we could introduce you to him and you could sort of soften him up a bit."

"A woman-hater, is he?" Again that baffling little smile lifted the corners of Stella's exquisite mouth. "They're usually interesting. You think I could handle him, then."

"Sure of it," Julie grinned, and then the twins rushed into the room.

They took one look at their sister, gave her a casual "Hi" and turned their minds to other matters. Stella always appeared to be amused at their casual treatment, laughingly saying that after all she was really no different from the rest of the family. Only Stella knew if she herself believed that.

"Nice bit of skunk," Tess commented, fingering the short mink coat Stella had carelessly draped over the back of a chair.

"That's a super drop of car," Tom breathed in an awed whisper, his nose flattened against the window. He was at an age where cars took precedence over everything else, even famous actress sisters and mink coats.

Stella gave him the famous smile the whole country had grown to know. "I'll give you a ride in it some time—if you behave yourself."

"I always behave myself—don't I?" he added indignantly, turning to Margaret Dermot for confirmation.

"Well, sometimes," his mother agreed dryly. She looked over at Stella, forgetting for a moment what she was about to say as her eyes drank in that sheer loveliness. It always puzzled her how she could have produced such a daughter. Then she recovered and mentally shook herself. "Your father's been kept late at the office... something absolutely unavoidable. He telephoned a few minutes ago."

"Never mind. It will give me a chance to make myself beautiful for him," Stella smiled.

They all laughed at the absurd idea of Stella having to make herself beautiful because she was so absolutely lovely already, and a few minutes later Stella caught up her mis-named mink and was led upstairs by Julie to freshen up. The twins departed for their favourite haunt, the garden, and Leigh and her mother stood at the foot of the stairs watching Julie prance up the stairs as if she was Tess's age, the years falling away from her with excitement, while Stella teased her with indulgent affection.

As they disappeared along the landing the two left down below looked at each other and smiled.

"It's good to have her back," Leigh said softly, and Margaret nodded.

"She's something to be proud of."

"And it hasn't changed her. That's what's so wonderful about it," Leigh added.

Margaret wiped away a surreptitious tear, then turned with an assumption of briskness towards her kitchen. "I think we'll have some tea. It's good for bringing people down to earth again." She bustled around, putting on the kettle, and then looked over at Leigh as the girl brought out cups and saucers and set them neatly on a tray. "You look a little tired. Ruiz Aldoret becoming more of a martinet than ever?"

Leigh smiled. "I expect it's all the excitement."

"Is he a martinet?"

"I suppose he is . . . a little, anyway."

"Then why don't you change your job?"

"I don't really mind working for him. He's all right once you get used to him." She frowned and shook her head with a puzzled glance at her mother. "Sometimes I even feel sorry for him."

"Sorry for him?" She set out biscuits in a dish with a rather surprised glance.

Leigh nodded. "It's silly, I know—he's rich enough to have almost anything he wants, but somehow, sometimes, I can't help feeling that he's not really happy underneath. Then, the next moment, he's the same as he always is, cold and hard, withdrawn—and I know I was just imagining things. It probably suits him to be as he is."

"Perhaps—or maybe he really is unhappy underneath. Even the rich have their problems, I suppose."

The kettle whistled shrilly and they turned their attention fully to the tea. When they left the kitchen and went along the corridor John Dermot was just entering the front door—and at that moment Stella appeared on the stairs, ran down them and held out her hands. He promptly engulfed her in a bearlike hug and laughed when she protested that he was crushing the velvet of her dress.

"Velvet doesn't crush nowadays," he said jokingly. "Leigh can tell you that, the sort of stuff they turn out at Merediths these days."

"Ah, yes, that famous boss of Leigh's." Stella turned her slightly mocking glance to her sister. "I have yet to meet him."

"You haven't missed anything, darling," Leigh said with a mock shudder. "He has a horrible way of looking right through you."

Just at that moment the doorbell rang and Tess raced to the door, calling out at the top of her powerful young lungs as soon as she opened it that Kerry had arrived. Kerry herself came in a moment later, following closely on the boisterous announcement of her arrival. Across the room her eyes met Stella's and instant antagonism flamed between the two. Stella hid hers very quickly, with practised ease that spoke well of her acting ability, but Kerry was not far behind.

"Hallo, Stella," she said smoothly. "I heard you were arriving today."

"For a whole fortnight," Julie chimed in happily, having followed her sister down the stairs.

A fortnight too long, Kerry thought grimly to herself. She had an odd feeling of dread. She neither liked nor trusted Stella, and probably the actress sensed it. That would account for the antagonism both had felt.

She looked over at her with concealed criticism, trying to find visible signs of the things she suspected, but there was nothing there. Stella looked perfect, and hardly older than she had when, just after her eighteenth birthday, she had coolly announced to her family that she had managed to get a film test and had then been offered a part in a film. That was six years ago. Now she was famous. Her small, exquisite body and perfect features, the glossy black hair and slightly slanting green eyes, assisted by undoubted acting ability, had taken her to the very top of the ladder.

Rich and famous—but she never forgot her family and they all loved her all the more for it.

Only Kerry had a suspicion that Stella Dermot had a different reason for coming home, and if she had been unwise enough to suggest that the actress merely visited her family because it suited her to do so and not because they really meant anything to her, they would have indignantly denied it, and her friendship with Leigh, which meant quite a lot to her, would no doubt be broken. So she kept silent, even if she was perfectly convinced in her own heart that Stella never had had much time for her family, except to serve her own interests—and she still felt the same way about them. They might one day be of use to her, so she did not break with them entirely. It was also good publicity. She liked to be kept in the public eye as the small town beauty who had become famous but did not forget her family. It was exceedingly good publicity, it served her well—or undoubtedly Stella Dermot would have shaken the dust of Korveston, the small Kentish town where she had grown up, off her expensive, dainty shoes and forgotten she had ever been there.

Now she was home for a fortnight—and she was going to cause mischief of some kind. Kerry did not know yet what form it would take, but it would come as surely as the sun set each night, and it was Leigh who caused her the most concern.

She did not know, but intuition told her what Stella would have been like as a child, reaching out greedy hands to her sister's toys, always being given them, because she was so beautiful and they had adored her even then. After a time she would always have lost interest in what she had taken and she would have dropped it, for its real owner to pick up again if they wanted to—but the toys would have been ruined by then. She was certain of it. There would have been a teddy bear with its eyes pulled out and perhaps some of its stuffing removed, a beloved doll that had lost its head or had its china body smashed. She would never have been spanked or reprimanded, though, because she was Stella, beautiful Stella.

It was about twenty minutes later that the doorbell rang again and Leigh went to let Bruce in. He was a sturdily built, rugged-faced man of twenty-six—just a year older than Leigh—and could not by any stretch of imagination have been called handsome. Neither was he particularly graceful, but there always seemed to Leigh to be something inherently sincere and dependable about him. Kerry on the other hand again had her own opinion. She liked Bruce well enough, but she sometimes suspected that he had a streak of weakness in him, allied to a peculiar and probably unpleasant obstinacy that would come out most when he was in the wrong. However, he was Leigh's choice and she loved him deeply, so Kerry again kept silent.

Leigh brought him in and introduced him to Stella with smiling pride, and at last Kerry knew what she had feared, because Stella looked at the brown-haired, rugged-faced man and smiled, softly and silently.

"Not him," Kerry prayed desperately. "Not him too."

The teddy bear, the broken doll—and now the man Leigh loved. Stella would take him, too.

CHAPTER 3

RUIZ ALDORET had a problem. It came in the form of the letter that he held between thin, strong hands and in one swift blow it broke down the barrier he had erected ten years ago. It all came back, the rush of longing for that beautiful white house surrounded by tall trees and masses of flowers, for the cool wind that sighed down from the mountains.

He looked down at the letter again and it told him the same thing. He was rich already, Merediths had given him that, but the letter gave him more—on one condition.

He could inherit the fabulous fortune he had once given up; he could go back to that white house he always dreamed of—but there was still the condition.

He had to be married when he went back—and he must not marry Mercedes Lastro.

If he tried to contest the will, he would immediately lose the inheritance, which would go instead to specified charities. The condition gave him three months, during which time he must marry, if not already married, and bring his bride to Carastrano, or give up again what he had already given up in the past.

Old Diego Aldoret had known his grandson well when he banked on the younger man doing anything in his power to possess the home and estates he had loved so much as a child.

Ruiz looked down at the letter again, the cold sharpness of his brain throwing off the confusion that learning of the condition had brought. The will could not be contested, so there must be another way out. He read it through again. It said that he must be married within three months of the reading of the will, if he was not already married, and he knew quite well what that was supposed to mean. An heir for Carastrano.

The thin lips set grimly. He wanted Carastrano, but he

had no intention whatsoever of being forced to set aside the decision he had made so long ago, that no woman should ever come to mean anything to him again.

His eyes narrowed, reading the letter through for the third time. Perhaps there *was* a way out. It made no mention whatever of the future of his marriage, nor of the type of person he should marry, except that it must not be Mercedes Lastro—and he had no wish whatsoever to marry Mercedes Lastro.

He also had no wish to get married at all. Nothing had been further from his mind the previous day. On the other hand, he wanted Carastrano.

The thin lips set again, as he remembered the man who had made that damnably unwelcome provision in the will. Diego Aldoret had always been a strong-willed martinet and no doubt he thought he could still get away with it, even after death.

There was, however, a way—a way that would comply in every word with the provision of the will, give him back the home he had loved so much, and yet at the same time allow him to retain the emotional invulnerability he prized so much.

A purely business arrangement for two people, enabling each to retain their freedom and go their separate ways once the purpose of the marriage had been fulfilled. That it was an empty compliance with the conditions of the will did not bother him at the moment. He was too coldly furious that the hand that had once had the power to rule his life and strip from him everything he had been used to—break away the very foundations of his life—should try to interfere once more, across a long period of years and even beyond death.

A cold smile gleamed in his eyes. For once in his life Diego Aldoret had made a mistake. He should have set out that provision in more complete detail. Now it would be quite simple to circumvent it—but he had to think of a girl who would be willing to enter into such a cold-blooded arrangement, a girl who was enough like him to have no use or place in her life for romance and who could be counted on to keep sentimentality out of the arrangement for the time they would have to spend together in Mexico.

But was there such a girl?

The thought pulled him up sharply. There was—the girl in the office adjoining his. Cool, so composed she sometimes hardly seemed human. Never once had she shown a flicker of anything that approached the laughing nonsense of some of the girls in the outer office, who occasionally annoyed him with their meaningless chatter—not that he ever heard much of it. There was only the impression of subdued silence if he ever ventured into her office. No doubt they had been chattering about their boy-friends, about romance and life in general—but not Leigh Dermot. She seemed altogether divorced from the sickly sentimentality that annoyed him, her eyes fixed on a career and no doubt clear-minded enough to see the advantages of a business arrangement of the sort he desired.

He reached out a hand to the buzzer on his desk and, without the least suspicion in her mind of how different was his purpose in calling her into his office from the usual one, Leigh picked up notebook and pencils and went in. She sat down in her usual chair and opened her notebook, knowing that it was at about this time he usually dictated his letters, then left her alone for the rest of the day unless something urgent arose.

He frowned, rustled the stiff paper of a letter in his hands, then started to speak, and Leigh, whose thoughts were for once elsewhere and not concentrating on her work, automatically took down what he said without actually realising what it was.

Then she translated her shorthand.

Ruiz Aldoret watched her closely, but the only outward sign of her amazement he could detect was a slight narrowing of her eyes. Leigh, however, wondered if she had gone completely crazy. Pink-eyed frogs stared up at her from her notebook, little blue lambs gambolled over it—or they could have done. They would not have been any sillier or more ridiculous than what she had written down while her thoughts were wandering.

She pulled herself together and looked up. "I'm afraid I didn't catch what you said, Mr. Aldoret." It certainly could not have been what she had written down in her notebook.

His expression became slightly sardonic. "I think you did.

I asked whether you would consider a purely business proposal of marriage."

Leigh looked back at her notebook. That was what she had written—and she had not been dreaming. Before she could gather her wits about her, he went on:

"Perhaps I should explain more fully before you say anything. I have recently been left my grandfather's estates in Mexico, but to claim them I have to fulfil certain conditions, otherwise everything goes to various specified charities."

"Certain conditions?"

Leigh heard her voice, quite cool and composed, repeating the words, and wondered how on earth she could sound so detached and unruffled after such an amazing "business proposition."

"I must be married. It would, of course, be only a temporary arrangement."

He watched her again and for a moment felt a stir of curiosity. Was she really as unemotional and detached as she appeared, or was it a perfect mask? Even someone completely devoid of human emotion would have shown surprise at his amazing proposal, but beyond the slight narrowing of her eyes, she had made no sign and he might have been talking about the weather.

Leigh meantime gathered together the remnants of her shocked wits and answered quietly, showing none of the slight indignation she felt that he considered she would even have contemplated such a proposal.

"I'm sorry, but I'm already engaged."

This time it was he who felt the shock of the unexpected, and he looked at her again, his curiosity growing stronger as he remembered her voice in Ricki's, lighter, younger, bubbling with amusement, and wondered again whether it was only a mask she wore in the office. Then he dismissed it with an impatient mental shrug, because he really had no interest in her personally.

"It is in that event quite impossible. As to your own engagement, do you intend to continue working after you are married, or will you leave?"

"I shall leave eventually, of course. No date has been set for my marriage yet, so I hadn't yet made any arrangements about leaving. I intended to give you plenty of notice, though, so you would be able to find somebody to replace me."

He nodded thoughtfully. "Of course. But I don't quite know what will be required now. I have decided to accept an offer to buy the factory. The new owners will need to make their own arrangements about staff, but they would probably want you to stay on for as long as you can."

"We hadn't thought of getting married for a couple of years yet," Leigh explained.

The faintly sardonic smile crossed his face again. "You apparently believe in long engagements."

"I think they're wise, even though both people can be quite sure. Marriage is too big a thing to just rush into. We're both saving until we can get a proper home as well."

It was all too sane and practical. Apparently he had been right about her in the first place. There was very little sentimentality or romance in her. For a moment he wondered about the man she was going to marry—was he just as restrained and practical?—then he dismissed them both from his mind, picked up a letter and started dictating, just as if nothing out of the ordinary had been said.

Leigh, on the other hand, could not quite get it out of her mind, because in some strange way it indefinably altered him. She looked at him with new eyes, for the first time really noticing the dark attraction Julie had teased her about.

In a way, he was the most attractive man she had ever seen, with the lithe, rather pantherish grace that some tall men possess and a proud way of holding his dark head. Both hair and eyes were as black as jet, with the light sometimes catching a blue sheen in his hair—but those dark eyes bore no resemblance whatever to the velvety soft southern eyes so beloved of romantic novelists. They were sharp and remote, as coldly chilling as black ice. The same chill lay over undoubtedly attractive features that were as sharply defined as a hawk. If that cold gravity ever broke, it was usually only into sardonic, rather mocking amusement that somehow suggested an undercurrent of bitterness.

As he picked up another letter, she looked down at his hands and saw that they were slender and beautifully formed, aristocratic hands, with thin, tapering fingers, then she looked up at his face again, as he spoke on the telephone, and wondered if those rather fine dark eyes had ever softened, or whether he had always been like this. Wondered if that sharp, incisive voice, with its faint suggestion of not exactly an accent but a deep musical intonation of "difference" had also ever softened—perhaps for a woman? Had it even been a woman who had made him like this? It did not seem possible though that any woman could ever have had that much power over him—yet in another man that peculiar stiffened curve to his rather too firm mouth might have been taken as an indication of deep, strong feelings too long repressed. Not in Ruiz Aldoret, though. Even if it had once denoted passion, such things were now long behind him.

Rather oddly, she found herself wondering what it would have been like had she been in a position to accept such a cold-blooded proposal. Rather horrible, probably. Three months spent in avoiding each other, then a quick annulment. A business contract from start to finish, making a mockery of the very meaning of marriage.

"I pity the girl who does decide to take on the job," she thought rather grimly, and yet she could not entirely put the thought of him from her mind for the rest of that morning, even though she typed as efficiently as usual, because when one has been shocked into thinking of a man as a possible husband, he never seems quite the same afterwards, even though it might have been a completely cold-blooded and unromantic situation from start to finish.

Leigh was in the hallway putting on her gloves ready to go to work when Julie wandered out from the breakfast room, watching her critically.

"I don't know why you have to wear such uninteresting clothes," she commented at last. "You always look so... so restrained."

"I couldn't exactly go to work in frills and furbelows," Leigh retorted with dry amusement. "Are you trying to tell me I look dowdy?"

"No, of course not," Julie denied instantly. She looked over at her sister who, as usual, was dressed in a neat, tailored skirt and crisp spotless blouse, with a lightweight summer coat over them. "But you always look so much like the perfect secretary," she added.

Leigh smiled down at her, amusement dancing in her deeply blue eyes. "That's what I try to be, my pet. I wouldn't last long if I wasn't. That boss of mine would soon turf me out on my ear."

Julie grinned involuntarily. "I'd like to see his face if he could catch you romping with the twins. It might change his ideas a bit."

Leigh tweaked one of her sister's long flying strands of hair in mock warning. "Don't you try matchmaking with him. You wouldn't stand a chance. I doubt if even our lovely Stella would manage to crash that steel wall around him—and in any case I want to marry Bruce, not a walking iceberg."

"Oh, I know you think he's just about the cats' whiskers ... but I don't think he's the right man for you," the incredible teenager told her in apparent seriousness.

"Oh, don't you!" Leigh retorted, more amused than anything else.

"No." Julie frowned and shook her head. "I sometimes think he's even a little bit in awe of you."

"Bruce in awe of me? Don't be so silly, Julie!"

Julie gave a wry little grimace. "Not really, I suppose, but sometimes you do seem ... well, too much the efficient secretary."

"You're just romantic," Leigh smiled. "If you think Ruiz Aldoret is a heart-throb you're certainly no judge of men."

"So you think I'm just imagining it about Bruce?"

Leigh smiled again. "Anyway, thanks for the warning. I'll dig out a plunging neckline next time I'm meeting him," she teased.

"Well, I still think that Ruiz Aldoret is marvellous," was Julie's parting shot as her sister went to the door.

"Then if you do come to work at Merediths, don't ever let him hear you say it, or you won't think it any longer," Leigh retorted, having the last word herself.

Yet, nevertheless, Julie's remark worried her and she thought about it deeply on the bus to work. There had been something just a little odd about Bruce lately. A hint of—what?

Was there anything in what Julie said? Was the "perfect secretary" attitude she assumed at work becoming a part of her, making her seem over-efficient, too controlled, even to Bruce? Did he even sense something lacking in her when he kissed her? Perhaps up against Stella's intense femininity she herself appeared slightly detached and even—horrible word—bossy. Yet he had seen her working in the garden in a pair of old shorts and blouse, smuts of dirt on her face and not at all like the "perfect secretary" Julie deplored. In case it was anything like that, she made a silent vow never to wear the strictly tailored clothes of the office when she was with Bruce.

At lunch time she was kept a little late after the hooter went and when she arrived at Ricki's Kerry was already there, esconced in their booth with Julie, who had been doing some shopping in town and had arranged to meet them for lunch. They were having a conference over the menu when Kerry noticed Leigh frowning to herself, almost unconsciously, it seemed.

So it had already started, she thought grimly to herself. Already Leigh was wearing a slightly puzzled look. Already she was biting her lip unconsciously, as she had frowned a moment ago. Was it just a general feeling of something wrong, or did she know that Bruce had been seeing Stella secretly? Probably not. It had only been sheer accident that had enabled Kerry to see them together, without them knowing. Previously she had lived on a farm and every so often she took a sentimental little journey out there, wandering through the fields and quiet country lanes. It was in one of those country lanes that she had seen Stella's car parked—and Bruce in it with her. They had been sitting decorously apart at the time, but Stella had the indefinable look of someone who had just been kissed.

Kerry had left as quietly as she had arrived, returning to the lodgings where she had lived since the farm had been sold on the death of her last surviving relative, sickness in her heart as she remembered the overheard huskiness in Bruce's voice during that brief moment she had come around the bend in the lane and seen the car. As she had turned away she had heard him speak again, telling Leigh's sister how beautiful she was—and Stella's husky, faintly mocking laugh. She did not look back, but the sudden silence had made her sure that they were no longer sitting decorously apart.

Oh yes, she was beautiful, Kerry thought grimly. But even a snake had a kind of hypnotic beauty, and in her opinion there wasn't much difference.

Their lunch had just been ordered when a neat dark head appeared through the curtains that screened the front of the booth.

"Ricki said you were here. Mind if I join you?"

She was quickly assured that they would be delighted if she would join them, and Janice Martin smiled as she sat down. She was a quiet, dark-haired woman of about thirty-five with a slow grave smile, one of the firm's most efficient outside workers, and the rumour was that, years ago, she had been jilted on the very eve of her marriage. Others said that her fiancé had been killed in a car crash the night before the wedding, but whatever the truth, she never spoke of it to anyone.

"So you're Julie," she said with a smile, when Leigh had introduced them. "I've been wanting to meet you. Leigh was always chattering about you when I was here three months ago."

"Oh dear!" Julie said apprehensively. "That sounds bad."

"Don't you believe it." She smiled over at the other two. "Anything momentous happen during my absence?"

"Well, Leigh went and got herself engaged," Kerry informed her.

Janice's face broke into a delighted smile. "Congratulations. It's Bruce, of course." She gave a little chuckle of laughter. "So he finally popped the question."

"Of course it's Bruce," Kerry retorted dryly. "She never had eyes for anyone else."

"And Ricki is going to give them Ernie as a wedding present," Julie chimed in, having already heard the story of the famous Ernie.

The elder woman raised a whimsical eyebrow. "Who on earth is Ernie?"

Julie chuckled. "The tea urn."

Kerry broke in, before Julie could make any more mysterious remarks. "Dear Bruce chose about the most unromantic spot he could possibly have decided on. We'd all come down here for dinner before going on to a show. We'd just finished and were standing up at the counter chatting to Ricki. We must have felt the radioactive elements around, because we shifted down, quite unconsciously, leaving him a clear field with Leigh." She grinned at Leigh's sudden uncontrollable blush. "Apparently the tea urn gave him courage and he popped the question then and there. So Ricki has promised to give them the urn in question as a wedding present."

Ruiz Aldoret never knew what made him go back to Ricki's. Perhaps it was the fact that the food was excellent and it was conveniently near—but it was quite unintentional that he again found himself eavesdropping, and this time his face broke into a quite involuntary smile that changed him altogether, because there was something absolutely ludicrous in the thought of the Englishman proposing among the cups and saucers and a tea urn. It was just as he had thought. His practical, efficient secretary had apparently chosen someone as unromantic as herself. Then, as he had once before, he shrugged off the thought of them. Or at least he meant to, but as before it again became quite unavoidable that he should listen to what they said.

"Trust him to pick the tea urn," Kerry remarked dryly. "He might have chosen moonlight and sweet music, or something like that—but no, he prefers tea urns!"

There was a soft chuckle of laughter and with some amazement Ruiz realised that it came from his secretary.

"Poor Bruce! They won't let him forget that for a long time."

Janice Martin shook her head, still smiling. "Well, not every girl can say that she's been proposed to among the tea urns." Abruptly her face sobered. There was a shadow of remembered bitterness in her eyes. "Sometimes these unromantic proposals turn out far better than the moonlight ones," she added quietly, and the other three remained silent. She went on, almost as if she was talking to herself. "Adrian was a real artist in these matters—but that didn't stop him eloping with a rich widow on the very eve of our wedding."

As she fell silent, Leigh asked softly: "Do you still miss him?"

Janice looked up and met her eyes. "I think I always shall—even though they were both killed in a car crash, on the very night that he jilted me." Then, as a little shudder ran through Julie, she smiled. "Now I'm scaring the poor child."

Julie shook her head. Her usually laughing face was more grave than any of them had ever seen it.

"No, I was just thinking how terrible it must be to go on loving someone all the time, knowing there was no chance of having your dreams ever come true."

Janice smiled, shaking her head. "It is terrible at first, my dear," she admitted, "but time dulls the edge." She made a quick gesture with one slender hand. "But don't let me put the damper on everyone. Hasn't anyone got something more cheerful to talk about?"

Leigh nodded, sensing that Janice wanted to turn the conversation into another channel herself.

"I have some news about Merediths. You'll probably see the notice this afternoon, but I might as well tell you now. It's going to be sold."

"Sold?" Kerry echoed blankly, and it was quite evident that the news had successfully banished all thought of the preceding conversation.

"He's apparently inherited some property in Mexico, so he's selling up and going back there."

She had no intention of saying anything about the terms of the will itself, because that was his own private business.

"Ye gods!" Julie broke in. "Don't tell me he's one of those real Spanish Dons."

"I didn't ask him," Leigh said dryly. "A lot of those old properties often do involve a title—though his full name is impressive enough on its own."

"Out with it!" Julie demanded.

"Ruiz Diego Palea de Aldoret," Leigh obliged.

Kerry whistled. "Quite a mouthful!" She glanced at her friend curiously. "How did you find out?"

"I've had to type different papers for him at odd times, to do with him staying in this country. He's not English, you know. He still retains his original nationality."

"A pity he doesn't act a bit more like it, then," Julie chimed in irrepressibly.

"It's just as well that he doesn't," her sister told her. "I can't imagine trying to work with a man chasing you round the office."

Julie chuckled. "I don't know. I think it would be rather fun—if it was Ruiz Aldoret."

"Oh, lord! Don't tell me the child really does have a crush on him," Kerry groaned.

"If she has, she'll soon get over it," Leigh said easily. "I don't think any girl could have a crush on that walking iceberg for very long."

"This is for all time," Julie corrected impressively, but with a chuckle in her voice.

"Yes, I know your crushes," Leigh retorted. "Remember the milk boy when you were fourteen? The world was almost at an end when he was transferred to another round—but it was surprising how quickly you mended after a trip to the fair."

Kerry gave her friend an amused glance. "I don't suppose even Ruiz Aldoret would feel complimented at being compared with the milk boy."

At that moment Ricki herself came in with their lunches. "By the way," she whispered, "did you know that your boss is occupying the next booth?"

"He's *what?*" came from Julie in a little shriek, and then a horrified silence fell. They glanced at each other and tried to remember what they had said.

Too much.

Leigh consoled herself with the thought that eavesdroppers never hear well of themselves, even unintentional ones. Then she thought of the other time he had been intending to visit Ricki's.

"Did he come here last Tuesday?" she asked softly, and Ricki nodded.

"I meant to warn you, but we were very busy at the time and it slipped my memory."

"Where was he sitting?" Leigh enquired, with a horrible certainty that it would be the same place he occupied today —right next to them—and last Tuesday, the day that Julie arrived home, had been when she had dissected the owner of Merediths with uncomplimentary frankness.

"Same place he is today," Ricki confirmed. "So I hope you didn't say anything too dreadful about him," she added in the same stage whisper, and then went away, leaving another of those horrified little silences behind her.

Janice looked from one to the other of them. "By the sudden ghastly silence I should imagine that you did say something rather dreadful," she whispered, and Leigh nodded, trying frantically to remember just what it was she had said that afternoon.

"Full attention to lunch from now onwards," Kerry muttered. Her glance over at Leigh sparkled with wry sympathy. "My condolences for having to face His Lordship this afternoon," she added *sotto voce*.

"I doubt if he would even deign to refer to it," Leigh assured her, in the same sort of low whisper. "If he heard anything before, he passed it by as beneath his dignity to comment upon. He'll probably do the same thing this time."

Yet nevertheless she found herself watching him closely when she went into his office that afternoon. There was, however, nothing at all different about him. He met her glance with the same cool indifference those dark eyes always possessed and, after the initial apprehension of facing him after what she had said about him at Ricki's, Leigh felt her embarrassment slide away.

Her transgressions, like a naughty child's, were to be allowed to slip away and be forgotten, she told herself with an inward chuckle.

Stella's visit was half way through, her family realised sadly. Another week and she would be gone, back to the busy exciting life that was hers. Reporters had besieged the rambling old house, taking pictures of Stella in the shabby, comfortable lounge, pictures of her standing roguishly on the twins' swing or draped invitingly against the trunk of an old apple tree, then she had banished them with sweet firmness, insisting that she now wanted her family left in peace and she would give them all another interview before she returned to London. Thereafter she remained in bed almost till lunchtime, arose languidly and lounged around the house. Sometimes she would take the twins for a run in her car after school—and in the morning the local paper would proudly present pictures of the famous actress with her young brother and sister. Or sometimes the pictures would be of her standing with her arm affectionately around Julie, or with Leigh and Bruce. Korveston loved it and so did the whole of the Dermot family.

On the evening of the same day when she had realised her comments about Ruiz Aldoret had been overheard, Leigh pushed open the back door to an accompaniment of wild yells from inside. She glanced over at her mother and Julie, who were preparing tea in the kitchen, smiling slightly.

"Sounds as if the Apaches are attacking again!"

She had no sooner spoken than a hideously painted Tom—streaked with a lipstick purloined from somewhere—waving a cardboard tomahawk, launched himself on her from ambush, clutched her around her waist to regain his balance, then did a complete turn around her, chasing an equally lipstick-streaked Tess who dashed in from the corridor dangling a handful of black string knotted together at the top as if it was someone's scalp. Nobody could say that Tess and Tom Dermot did not have vivid imaginations, even if they did tend to become a little lurid and gruesome on occasion.

Leigh eyed the 'scalp' dryly. "You gruesome little wretch!" she said to her youngest sister, who only grinned quite unrepentantly.

Julie, however, had other things on her mind. She had just been allowed to purchase her first lipstick and she grabbed hold of her brother with a cry of protest.

"That's my lipstick!"

"It's not lipstick," Tom denied, wriggling himself free from her hold. "It's Apache warpaint!" and he took off out into the garden after Tess with a bloodcurdling yell, Julie chasing after him as a third member of the hunt, in pursuit of her purloined lipstick.

As the racket died away into the distance Stella appeared in the kitchen doorway.

"Are they always so noisy?" she asked with a little shudder.

Margaret nodded with a little smile. "I'm afraid so."

"It's not so bad when they're stalking each other, it's when they break ambush that the noise starts," Leigh told her.

She went up to her room to hang up her coat and when she came down Stella was in the lounge.

"What have you been doing with yourself? I hope you haven't been bored?"

"Bored?" Stella looked across at her with a rather mocking light in her eyes. "Not yet, but I think I should be if I stayed too long. Don't you ever get tired of rusticating?"

Leigh smiled and shook her head. "I suppose the rest of the Dermot family were made to rusticate. It suits us to bask in your glory. We don't have to do anything strenuous ourselves."

Stella gave her a sardonic glance and lowered herself gracefully into an armchair.

"I wonder what it's like to be so content."

"Aren't you content?" Leigh asked her quietly.

"Content?" Stella gave a short, hard laugh. "You're only content when you're dead."

Leigh looked slightly shocked. "Stella!"

Stella gave her that mocking little smile again. "Shocked?" She shrugged. "I have so much, haven't I? I should be content—yet there's always the striving for more; always the need to keep at the top of the ladder. The new ones coming along, trying to pull you down, so you have to kick them back. Then somehow they get in and you have to fight harder than ever to stay where you are. I know," she finished broodingly. "I had to fight like that myself to get where I am."

"Why don't you give it up, then?" Leigh asked quietly.

"Give it up?" Stella gave her a startled look, then shrugged. "That would be even worse. I'd probably die of boredom."

"Not if you married and had a home of your own. Hasn't there ever been anybody you wanted to marry?"

Stella shrugged again. "Sometimes... until I grew bored with them." She gave a queer little twisted laugh. "I suppose if I do eventually find somebody, he'll already be claimed by some other female."

Leigh looked at her beautiful sister, quite shocked, and told herself wisely that success was not everything it seemed. Under everything she had, under all her gaiety, Stella was still not happy. One elusive something escaped her. Like Ruiz Aldoret. With all his riches and his position, there had always been the suspicion in her mind that he was not really happy. He too wanted something more, but he hid it behind a mask of self-sufficiency, not gaiety as Stella did. Of course it was hard to know with a man like Ruiz Aldoret. In his case it could be just imagination on her part and he was just as hard and emotionless underneath as he appeared on the surface.

A moment after that little mental remark she very nearly lost her balance. A very large and very exuberant white dog burst into the room, crossed it in one flying leap and planted his paws on her shoulders. The League of Nations, affectionately known as Snooks, had just realised that she was home and was greeting her in his usual fashion. After that of course there was no chance of any more serious conversation, and somehow she was rather glad of it. That odd little feeling of something wrong had returned to her.

The week drew on, interspersing the normal everyday happenings with the lingering pleasure of having Stella there. Julie was quite settled in at home by now and said it seemed as if she had never been away to boarding school. Flix, the household cat, presented everyone with a batch of ginger and white kittens and Snook cut his paw and had to be taken to the vet. Work went on just the same, life was just the same —until the evening before Stella was due to return to London.

Then everything changed . . . everything became different.

Bruce had a day off from work to replace a holiday he had worked through a few months ago doing urgent maintenance work, and they had arranged to go to a ball that evening. Ruiz, overhearing Leigh speaking to Kerry about it —he always seemed to overhear things at most unexpected times—had surprised her by telling her to go home an hour early so that she would have plenty of time to get ready. Afterwards she did not know whether she should thank him or hate him for sending her home early.

The house seemed quiet and still when she arrived home. Julie and her mother had intended to go to a film during the afternoon and had apparently not yet returned. The twins were remaining a little late at school practising for some parade. By the quietness, either Stella was also out or she was lying down, or perhaps reading.

Leigh opened the lounge door.

"We can't do this to her. I won't let you. I'd rather be unhappy for the rest of my life than hurt Leigh."

For a moment Leigh stood in the doorway struggling with the realisation that it was Stella's voice she heard—then she recognised the man who held her sister's slim, exquisite figure and bent his head to press his cheek against that flawless complexion with a little groan that explained far more clearly than any words.

Bruce.

CHAPTER 4

FOR one heartrending moment Leigh stood there, then she slipped out of the room automatically, as silently as she had entered, leaning back against the closed door as if she did not have the strength to move. She had heard of those moments when everything was supposed to stand still, but never thought she would actually experience one, that she would know the feeling of having everything she had dreamed of wiped away in a short instant of time.

Bruce did not love her. He was in love with Stella.

The scene she had interrupted could have no other meaning. They had been so engrossed in each other they had not even known she was there.

For a moment longer she stood on the other side of the door, one clenched hand pressed to her lips, trying to will herself to move, but she seemed frozen in the one spot, and even the house was silent and hushed. Homecoming was usually a time of noise and bustle, but today everything was different. Today was nothing like all those days that had come and gone before.

She had not felt any sense of warning as she left work, but the tensed, waiting feel of the house should have warned her. There had been no Snooks coming to greet her in bounding leaps—for some odd reason he did not like Stella and had apparently taken himself off somewhere in the garden—and even Flix and her five kittens had been asleep in the kitchen and had not bestirred themselves at her entry.

Perhaps if she had come in by the front door, instead of going round to the back entrance, perhaps if she had not left work early, then she might not have seen Stella in Bruce's arms, they would have heard her key in the front door... or perhaps not, since they had not even heard the lounge door open.

Finally she was able to make herself move. She turned slowly and went back the way she had come, out through the kitchen, along the pathway and into the street again. Then she stopped and numbly looked around her.

What was she to do now? She could not stand in front of the house like one of the flowering shrubs that the family tended with such loving care.

No, that would be altogether wrong, her dazed, shocked mind told her. She could not just stand there. People would look at her. She had to move, to walk—and so she walked, briskly, with quite automatic movements, without the least idea of where she was going.

How could she have been so blind, so smugly complacent in her own happiness, not knowing that two people she loved were so unhappy? It all came back to her now—the odd feeling of something wrong, Bruce's sometimes strained attitude. Most of all Stella—at last finding love, only to discover that it belonged to someone else and her own sister at that. Had some premonition been in her mind when she said that if she ever found the man she could believe in and trust, somebody else would already have claimed him?

Poor darling Stella. Unhappy and miserable herself, she could still think of the sister she would have hurt if she took her own happiness. And Bruce too. It was quite obvious that he thought the same way, refusing to break the engagement that would ruin his life too if it was allowed to continue. And it could not continue, of course. They could not be allowed to ruin their lives. However much pain it caused Leigh to give him up, it would be quite wrong if she tried to hold him. In any case, what happiness could there be for her in a marriage where she would know all the time that when Bruce kissed her he would be trying to pretend she was Stella and when she would know all along that she was cheating, that she could have allowed them to be happy?

She sighed and shook her head and her creamy brow furrowed as she walked with blind, brisk purpose. It seemed that somebody else watched out for where she went, seeing that she did not step into the road in front of a car—she was certainly not coward enough to think of anything like that—while her mind was completely occupied with what she would have to do.

What should she have done? Walked in while they were together? That would have forced the issue. Now it would be hard to bring up the subject in cold blood. But wouldn't it have been just as hard if she had tried to break the engagement on the spot? Stella might have still refused to marry Bruce, and that certainly could not be allowed to happen.

All the love she felt for her sister became concentrated in one resolve—to find some way out. It was better that two people be happy and only one hurt, rather than the other way round. In any case, she knew quite well that she would not be happy now even if she did marry Bruce. That would merely have made all three of them unhappy.

She went on walking, still briskly, still automatically, knowing that she had to find some way out before the shock could wear off and she became sunk in a stupor of despair. Her mind was oddly clear now, working quickly, with a strange, sharp clarity. It had to be now, she told herself, before she could give way to tears—but she could find no way out.

At last she had to return home and pretend that everything was normal. The rest of the family were home by then, but she cried out of going to the ball. She could not possibly have gone, and a headache was a good enough excuse. Intuition told her that Bruce was glad she had decided not to go.

Stella went back to London in the morning, while Leigh still sought around in her mind for some way to break off the engagement without giving them any cause to suspect that she might have found out about them. She could not break it off for no reason at all, nor could she pretend interest in somebody else, because the whole family knew she had never shown the slightest attachment to any other man. She had not even been in close contact with anyone else to be able to make a pretence of having fallen in love with him. There had only been her work—and Ruiz Aldoret—and in the evenings, Bruce.

Then suddenly it came to her. She heard Julie's teasing voice:

"I don't see how you could possibly have escaped falling in love with him."

The whole improbable, horrible answer was so clear there

was no need for any further thought. She would marry Ruiz Aldoret.

There was instant, rebellious withdrawal at the decision. She did not want to marry that cold, inhuman man who for three years had been nothing more to her than a sharp, incisive voice. She wanted warmth and love in her life, not an empty mockery for what no doubt would be a set period of time . . . and then finish.

It was inevitable that she get to know more about him, as they would no doubt be forced to live in the same house, but she was quite sure that she did not even want to know him. There was something repelling about that cold withdrawn personality, endurable at work, because there was never any need to forsake the impersonal, but what would it be like in a strange country, quite alone, married to a man who, in that moment, she almost hated?

She shivered, but nevertheless her resolve was unshaken. She did not say anything to the family or Bruce yet—she wanted to present them with a *fait accompli*—so first she had to wait until she could speak to Ruiz Aldoret.

She was unable to prevent herself shedding a few tears in the privacy of her room that night, but in the morning all desire to cry had gone. She was glad of the rigid self-control she possessed. It stood her in good stead now, strengthening the impersonal mask she always wore in the office so that she was able to knock at Ruiz Aldoret's door and enter quite calmly when he called out to her. It was only at that moment that it occurred to her that he might have found somebody else, but she shrugged it off. If he had, then she would just have to find some other way.

Quite involuntarily she found herself looking at him with more personal eyes, feeling again the shock of discovering that he was so very attractive, that he would be even magnetically so if he was not quite so cold and withdrawn.

Those sharp black eyes looked across at her with a question in them and she mentally braced herself.

"Mr. Aldoret, could I speak to you for a few minutes, if you're not too busy?"

"Of course." He nodded towards her usual chair. "Sit down."

There was only one way to do it, she thought as she sat

down. Be cool and unembarrassed, as if it was just the business proposition he had called it—and of course that was all it really was, even though it involved the closest tie possible between a man and woman.

"That business proposition you mentioned earlier—is it still open?" She hesitated, biting her lips in spite of her self-control. "Because . . . because if . . ."

"Because if it is you might have changed your mind?" he finished for her. The dark eyes raked her face searchingly, while remaining inscrutable themselves. "And your engagement?"

Leigh met his gaze with level composure. "It was broken off."

"Recently? Last night, for instance?"

"Yes," she confirmed quietly.

"I see." Again she was conscious of that dark, unreadable scrutiny. "And you have changed your mind about my proposition?"

"Yes," Leigh said again, resisting the absurd desire that came to her to giggle childishly, because that word 'proposition' sounded so odd. Somehow she had always associated that particular word with blondes, diamonds, mink and illicit love affairs, none of which could remotely fit the present situation. Love affairs in particular, illicit or otherwise, were totally out of place when thought of in conjunction with Ruiz Aldoret. Then that reminded her of another thing. "People wouldn't have to know that it was only a business proposition, would they?" she asked. The whole idea of any sort of love affair between Ruiz Aldoret and herself might appear to her as completely ridiculous, but Bruce and Stella had to be made to believe just the opposite, and if there was even a rumour of the true position that would make the whole idea quite useless.

"I have no wish myself that it should become public knowledge," he answered calmly. "At present only the solicitors and myself are aware of the conditions of the will, beside yourself, of course."

"What exactly would be required?" Leigh asked, carefully controlling her voice, so that it still sounded cool and businesslike.

"Part of it you know already. After the marriage some

time will have to be spent at Carastrano, to give it the appearance of being a normal marriage. Afterwards, when the terms of the will have been complied with, a quiet annulment could be arranged. There can be no legal quarrel with that. Any marriage can be found to be a failure."

"That sounds quite . . . acceptable."

The inscrutable mask of his expression broke slightly and one dark brow flicked up in rather sardonic amusement.

"Don't you want to know the terms first?"

"Terms?" Leigh gave him a startled glance.

"I naturally would not expect you to go through with this for nothing. It is, after all, a buisness proposition."

"I hadn't really thought about it," she said slowly—and then an audacious and quite outrageous idea occurred to her. "If . . . if there was to be any payment involved, I would rather it was . . . it was in some other form."

His expression closed up again; the sardonic amusement was gone. "Such as?" he asked evenly.

"Would you pretend to be in love with me?"

There was a shocking little silence, and as it dragged on for what seemed like hours she would have given anything to withdraw those unpardonable words. She did not dare to look at his face, staring down at her hands, clenched in her lap, as if that was the most important thing in the world, while inwardly she quaked and shrank from the blast of icy contempt she was sure would fall on her at any moment now. Then—

"Just why was your engagement broken?" he asked, and that was the last thing she had expected to hear.

The surprise of it made her glance quickly at his face, but his expression was still quite inscrutable, so she could not judge what sort of reaction might be greeting her request. She wondered now how she could possibly have had the temerity to have actually said it.

"Does that matter?" she countered after a moment.

"No—unless this is an attempt to make your ex-fiancé jealous."

Make Bruce jealous? Even try to prevent him reaching happiness with Stella when she loved them both so much? It was such a horrible and insulting idea that her eyes started to sparkle a little, and anyone who knew her better than this man would have taken that as a warning.

"Once you enter into this arrangement," he continued, "I shall expect you to go through with it—not break it off at the last moment."

"He's marrying my sister," Leigh told him restrainedly.

"Oh, I see," he said—and then it happened.

"You don't see anything of the kind," she burst out furiously, guessing what he was thinking, and the very idea that she should be using him to get Bruce back was so unthinkable that it totally banished all vestige of embarrassment that her unthinking request had given rise to. "You don't see anything at all," she repeated. "I happen to love my sister very much, and to get her to believe that I don't love Bruce any more, I shall have to tell her that I want to marry someone else." She gave a short, hard laugh. "Don't worry, I'll go through with it."

Ruiz leaned back in his chair slowly, watching her all the time. His expression was still as unreadable as ever, but there was half-veiled curiosity in his eyes now.

So she was not entirely the emotionless creature he had once thought her. Those dark blue eyes were glowing with what could only be unshed tears—but, even as he watched, she bit her lips almost viciously and went on in the type of voice he was used to hearing from her. That rigid self-control for the first time began to intrigue him.

"I apologise for the outburst," she said quietly. "But at least you understand now exactly how matters stand. I'm still in love with my fiancé—I haven't yet broken off the engagement—but this will give me an excuse to do so."

"You're absolutely sure that it is necessary?"

Leigh nodded. "Absolutely sure," she said evenly. "I happened to . . . to overhear something and I have no intention of allowing them to spoil their lives by fostering any ridiculous ideas of duty towards me. This is the only way I can really convince them, so I shall certainly not be the one to back out."

"You show remarkable altruism in the circumstances," he remarked, and Leigh gave him a surprised glance.

"Do I? I don't see that I could have acted in any other way."

Perhaps you couldn't, he said to himself, beginning to form an entirely new picture of his efficient, impersonal secretary, who was nowhere near so unemotional as he had thought her. Then the glint of sardonic amusement returned to his eyes.

"I wonder that you trust me to play such a role, considering the opinion you expressed one day at Ricki's," he commented with bland deliberation.

Leigh felt herself flush a vivid crimson. "Then you did hear!"

"I heard quite a lot," he confirmed dryly. "It was quite a sweeping condemnation. Is that what you really believe of me?"

"Of course not," Leigh denied hastily, trying to think just what she had said that dreadful lunchtime. She couldn't think of anything in particular, but everything she had said she had certainly agreed with at the time and found no reason to believe differently now. With a mental shake of her head she decided she should never have made the suggestion. Quite apart from the audaciousness of her request, she could not for one moment imagine him being able to carry it out.

Ruiz, reading her mind more accurately than she realised, elevated that sardonic black brow again.

"I think, in spite of opinions to the contrary, I could manage a little play-acting—but what about yourself?" and he shot the question at her so quickly and unexpectedly that Leigh felt herself flushing again—and for the first time thought about her own side of the bargain.

When she had first made her fantastic suggestion, she had not thought of the personal aspects of it—and how on earth was she going to pretend to be in love with someone like Ruiz Aldoret? She hastily stifled her new trepidations though and made herself shrug calmly.

"I think I could manage it. People are rarely demonstrative in public, so I don't think very much would be needed."

"In that case, we can take the matter as settled," he said, and that was all the reaction she received to her fantastic request, when she had expected contemptuous refusal. Beyond making sure that it was not just an attempt to make Bruce jealous, he had concurred with almost insulting indifference. "We can be married at the end of the month, if that suits you," he continued crisply, just as if there was nothing personal in it at all. "There seems to be nothing to be gained by waiting. Arrangements are already well in hand for the sale of the factory." He had been looking down at one of the papers on his desk on the last words, but he glanced up at her again, with a slight frown drawing his black brows together. "I don't suppose you know any Spanish, so it would be as well if you took a few lessons. You will find it quite useful as you will be spending some months at least at Carastrano. All expenses will, of course, be covered, and I will also arrange for a lump sum to be transferred to you."

"But I said I didn't . . ." Leigh began, but he cut her off with a quick gesture of one slim, long-fingered hand, an alien, un-English gesture that made her conscious of his Latin blood, something she quite often forgot, in spite of his darkness.

"It is quite out of the question," he said firmly. "I said that this was to be a business proposition. The other is quite beside the point."

"Very well." She shrugged almost indifferently. "I leave that entirely to you."

He reached out a hand to the telephone. "I will make arrangements for you to have some Spanish lessons. There is quite a good school . . ."

"I can already speak Spanish."

For the first time since she had worked with him, Leigh had the satisfaction of seeing his composure momentarily broken.

"You can speak it already?" He had control of himself almost immediately and switched to the language she claimed to have knowledge of. "What made you learn it?"

Leigh hesitated, quite aware that, by speaking it himself, he expected her to reply in the same language, possibly to test the truth of her assertion and how well she did speak it.

"I once intended to go for a holiday in either South America or Mexico," she answered carefully, and was surprised to see him smile in a way that transfigured his whole face.

"You have quite a good accent."

"Thank you," Leigh replied, still amazed at the difference a smile could make. It was the first time she had ever seen him smile other than mockingly or with rather sardonic amusement.

"You never did go?"

Leigh shook her head. "I intended to go last year, but..."

"But you became engaged instead?" he supplied, switching back to English as she broke off. "I must confess to having a very high regard for Mexico," he added, as she nodded in confirmation of his remark. "It should be interesting to show you the places I once used to know so well myself."

All at once the totally impersonal aspect of it was gone and she did not know quite how it had happened, when not even the impossible bargain she had made with him had been able to do it. The whole matter now did not seem quite so horrible as it had only a short while ago and she looked at him with some curiosity that must have been apparent in her expression.

He gave her an enquiring glance in return. "Something puzzles you?"

"No, not really," Leigh denied quickly, and then she added, when she had certainly decided to let the matter pass, "I just thought that you seemed a...a little different. It didn't seem quite so cold-blooded and horrible."

"Horrible?" Then he shrugged. "I suppose it is in a way, but there is no reason why we should not be friends, is there? It is perhaps also a necessity, considering the part we shall have to play," he added, with a species of sardonic amusement that again sent the colour flying to her cheeks.

"Yes...yes, of course," she said confusedly.

"I must also confess to finding you not quite what I expected," he commented urbanely, and Leigh gave him an almost startled glance.

"I suppose all of us are not quite what we appear on the surface," she said after a moment, wondering what this man was really like under the surface. She was beginning to suspect that her original opinion of him was not quite correct.

"True enough," he agreed. "I think you had better tell me something about your family." Again there was that hint of sardonic amusement. "It will seem strange if I know nothing about them."

That brought her up against another problem. He would have to meet her family, and she did not know how they would react to each other. For three years he had seemed a withdrawn, unapproachable man, and now, in the space of only a few minutes, she had already seen two different facets of his unknown real self, the momentary softening when he had complimented her on her accent and in speaking of his old home, and the sardonic mockery which she was discovering had the power to break the composure she had always managed to keep intact even during any business upsets.

Then she saw his waiting glance on her, seeming to indicate that he was a busy man, even though these personal details did have to be attended to, and quickly launched into a short description of her family.

"And Stella is the sister who caused you to break your engagement," he commented when she had finished. He showed no sign of surprise or even interest that the famous Stella Nordett was her sister.

Leigh nodded in silent confirmation, not trusting herself to speak just at that moment, because all the pain of her broken engagement rushed back and she had to hide it from him, especially as she had an uncomfortable suspicion it would be greeted with that rather jibing amusement she was beginning to be afraid to call forth. He was a man who would have no patience with broken hearts.

Shortly after that the whole amazing interview was over, except that he insisted they should lunch together, so that the office could get some intimation of what was coming—and Leigh knew quite well the shock that was going to be to everyone.

The worst part was yet to come though, breaking the news to Bruce and making him believe it—or was the worst part really further off still, when she had to start playing the part she herself had insisted upon. That surely would be the hardest of all—in love with Bruce and forced to pretend to love a man she did not even feel at ease with.

She did not say anything when she reached home, but waited until Bruce came round to collect her to go to a film they had previously arranged to see. He looked tired and slightly haggard and she was glad that at last she would be able to give him new hope.

They had not gone very far from the house, Bruce intent

on his driving, when she broke the somewhat strained silence between them.

"Will you stop the car? There's something I want to say to you."

Bruce threw her a swift glance, then swung the little car into a deserted side street and switched off the engine. He turned to her then, waiting.

"I want you to release me from our engagement," she said abruptly, and felt him start at her side.

"Release you?"

"Yes." She gave a quick little shrug which she hoped would pass as well contrived in the semi-darkness. "I thought it would work out, but I can see now that... well, that there's no chance of a marriage between us succeeding."

Bruce was silent for a long time, then he moved, turned so that he could look at her directly.

"What caused this sudden decision?"

Leigh gripped her hands tightly together in her lap and managed the supreme lie.

"I'm ashamed to have to admit it, but I didn't love you even when I first became engaged to you. There was... someone else, but I didn't think there was the remotest chance of him loving me in return. Now I know there is, and..." She broke off with another of those appealing little gestures. "I just can't go on with it."

"Who is it?" Bruce asked abruptly.

"Ruiz Aldoret."

"Ruiz Aldoret?" His shocked surprise was almost insulting to the other man. "Are you serious?"

"Quite serious." She bit her lips again with every appearance of being near to tears, which she was, but from another reason. "I didn't want to hurt you like this... but I fell in love with him three years ago. Nobody guessed, not even Ruiz himself." She managed to get his name out somehow, but wondered if she would be able to do it to his face. Then she pulled off her ring, with its small, sparkling diamond, which she always wore in the evening, after she left work, and handed it to him, while her finger felt suddenly bare and naked.

Bruce took it almost unconsciously. "This doesn't have anything to do with... Stella?"

"Stella?" She managed to instil just the right amount of bewilderment into her voice. "What on earth could Stella have to do with it?"

"Well, I thought... I mean it's nothing to do with Stella and myself, is it?"

"Stella and yourself?" Leigh repeated, as if she could not understand what he was hinting at.

Bruce hesitated, looking uneasy, then blurted out, "Stella and I... we discovered we were in love, but she wouldn't let me tell you."

"Stella and you?" Leigh echoed, as if completely thunderstruck, then somehow or other she forced a delighted little laugh. "Oh, that's wonderful! Now I don't have to feel ashamed of breaking off the engagement like this." Then she allowed her voice to grow serious. "What do you mean—she wouldn't let you tell me?"

"She wouldn't break up your engagement, said it was better for things to be as they were before she came home."

"And you let her go back to London with things like that between you...." She broke off, biting her lip in apparent contrition. "I'm ashamed of myself for not noticing before. You must have been very unhappy . . . all because of me."

"It doesn't matter, not any more," and he kissed her more sincerely than he had for some time. It was that which destroyed the illusion she had so carefully built up. Horrified, she felt her lips cling to his involuntarily, and when he put her from him a moment later she could have cried with mortification and self-disgust.

"It was all a pack of lies, wasn't it?" he said quietly. "You did know—and how does Ruiz Aldoret come into it?"

Leigh bit her lip. "I thought it would make it easier for you and Stella." She saw a look of enquiry begin to form on his face and nodded. "Yes, I really have agreed to marry Ruiz Aldoret."

"But you're not really in love with him."

"No, but it doesn't matter."

"Doesn't matter?" he echoed. "You can't make a marriage like that! Stella wouldn't..."

"Stella mustn't know anything about it," Leigh interrupted firmly. The only way now seemed to be to tell him the truth, and she did so, quickly. "So you see it's only a business proposition. It doesn't involve any question of permanency."

He still seemed disposed to argue, but at last she managed to convince him that it had to go on as she had arranged. She could not possibly marry him now, and if Stella knew the truth it was more than likely that she would still refuse to marry him. The only way was to make her sister believe that the marriage to Ruiz Aldoret was a normal one.

"You've got to make her believe that," Leigh said urgently. "It's the only way now. She mustn't know anything about ... about the time I came home early. I've taken it so far—and in any case I couldn't let Ruiz Aldoret down now. It won't hurt me, won't alter anything—just a business arrangement—but it will make Stella happy and not blame herself. You can see the way she's taken it already."

"I suppose so," he agreed reluctantly. "But I don't like to see you doing anything. . . ."

"It's the only way," Leigh repeated firmly. "And you mustn't tell Stella a thing about it being only a business proposition. Promise me that."

"All right," he said at last, and on that note they decided to return home, since neither of them were in any mood to watch the rather sentimental film they had been going to see. When the car drew up at the gate, he turned to her quickly.

"Would you like me to come in and break the news for you?"

Leigh shook her head. "No, I'd rather do it myself."

Before he could argue, or make any other suggestion, she said goodnight quickly and went inside. Snooks greeted her with his usual exuberant bound and, with a great effort of will, she managed to assure him that his boisterous affection was returned. She had to act like somebody who was perfectly happy, so she might as well start now.

When she entered the lounge she was glad to find that only her mother and Julie were there, the twins having been banished up to bed.

Margaret looked up with a smile. "We thought you were going to the cinema. Changed your mind?"

"Yes." She paused. Again it must be done bluntly, as she had nerved herself to speak to Ruiz and also to Bruce—but this time the pretence had to succeed. She must not give herself away with anyone else. "I'm not engaged to Bruce any more," she said with quiet composure, and held out her bare left hand for them to see.

A shadow of worry instantly descended on her mother's face. "Not . . . engaged to Bruce?"

Leigh shook her head, smiling at her mother. "We decided it was a mistake." She even laughed slightly. "Don't look so worried. It's not the end of the world."

"But you said . . ."

"I'm ashamed to admit that I said a lot of things that were not the truth," Leigh assured her quietly. "I don't love Bruce and never have done." As she spoke the words she half expected to hear the cock crow at any moment.

There was a little pause. "Perhaps you'd better tell us just what did happen," Margaret said quietly after a moment.

"There's not really very much to say." Leigh tried to keep all her facts marshalled. The worst of entering into any kind of deception was that one had to remember exactly what had been said. "I've been trying to bring myself to tell Bruce for quite some time," she went on. "Then something happened today and I knew I had to scrape up the courage to let him know I couldn't marry him, that I wanted to marry someone else instead." She paused, then added, feeling the bridges burn behind her, "Ruiz Aldoret."

"Ruiz Aldoret?" Julie almost squeaked.

"Ruiz Aldoret?" Margaret echoed more quietly, but there was a look of shock in her eyes. Probably, remembering her daughter's descriptions of the owner of Merediths, she was wondering how anyone could want to marry that cold, withdrawn man, in spite of the fact that he was supposed to be more than normally attractive. "This is rather . . . unexpected," she added haltingly, and Leigh gave her an apologetic glance.

"I wish I could have given you some hint before, but it was quite impossible."

"You really are going to marry him?" Julie asked on a gasp.

Leigh nodded. "We shall be announcing our engagement very soon and we don't intend it to be a long one. We're going to be married at the end of the month."

Then, of course, she had to bring out the careful little

story she had prepared for them, all about having been in love with Ruiz almost from the very first moment of going to work at Merediths, but thinking it was useless to hope that it would ever come to anything. It was strange how easy she found it now, as if the fact that she had to play a part—and play it well—had made a difference. She would probably have succeeded in keeping up the deception with Bruce too if he had not kissed her in gratitude for receiving his freedom. She still hated herself for allowing Bruce to guess, but it would work out all right if Stella did not find out.

It was strange—and even a little frightening—to realise that she would very soon be tied to a man who was almost a stranger to her personally, in a bond that, although on the surface was one of the closest there could be between a man and woman, was in reality a complete farce. She could not imagine trusting another man to keep it completely impersonal, but the thought of Ruiz Aldoret doing otherwise was laughable.

"But you never gave the slightest indication before of how you felt," Julie said curiously. "That day in Ricki's you thoroughly pulled him to pieces."

"I had to. The least thing might have attracted his attention. You know how gossip spreads in a large firm. Suppose somebody had heard me agree with what you said. The next thing would have been a rumour that I was in love with him."

"I suppose so," Julie agreed.

Margaret smiled at her eldest daughter, shaking her head with a touch of puzzled surprise still evident.

"It's most unexpected, my dear," she repeated, "but if it's what you really want, I'm glad it turned out this way." She turned to Leigh with her smile becoming a little mischievous. "When are we going to see this rather impressive Ruiz Aldoret?"

"Soon, I hope."

"Oh, lord!" Julie burst out in sudden dismay. "What's it going to be like having the boss for a brother-in-law?" She gave her sister a wicked grin. "Don't you feel like the office girl being cheeky when you call him by his first name?"

"Something like that," Leigh admitted, certainly not intending to reveal that she had never yet called him by his christian name. Even so, she was quite sure that it was going to be just as Julie said. She was going to feel like a very junior office girl caught in a flagrant impertinence—but having to pretend to be in love with him was going to be even worse. It was positively terrifying.

Later there was the job of breaking the news to John Dermot, and Leigh wondered how her father would take it.

The bushy eyebrows drew together in a frown when Margaret told him. "She's going to do what?" he demanded, and Leigh flushed and bit her lip. His tone was not exactly encouraging. It would be awkward if Ruiz was met with veiled hostility. But she need not have worried. Those penetrating eyes, of the same dark blue that she had inherited, fixed on her for a long searching moment, then surprisingly he nodded with complete approval. "Good man. Couldn't have chosen better for you myself."

"Well!" his wife said indignantly. "You might at least show a little surprise."

"Why?" he demanded. "He's the sort of man she should marry. Bruce wants to lean on people."

So that was his opinion of Bruce? Strange how one found out how people really felt about things when something like this happened. How would he take the news of Bruce and Stella becoming engaged? She had decided not to tell them herself. It would be better if it eventually came from either of the two concerned.

After that, of course, the same story had to be retold, while all the time she felt bitterly ashamed of herself for becoming such a good liar. She even embroidered it a little this time, telling them that the knowledge that he was selling the factory and returning to Mexico had made Ruiz realise that he would never see her again and, being unaware of her engagement since she never wore her ring for work, he had taken her by surprise by suddenly asking her to marry him.

Even if she had given herself away to Bruce, it was becoming so easy to convince everyone else that she found it giving rise to a terribly guilty conscience. Afterwards she went to bed and cried softly into her pillow, hoping that by the morning it would be dry and not give the lie to the performance she had put on. In any case, she always made her own bed, so there was little likelihood of anyone noticing, even if it was still damp.

After a little while, when she finally managed to control her tears, she turned over on her back and stared up at the ceiling. Well, it was done. Everyone now knew she was going to marry Ruiz Aldoret instead of Bruce.

On the way to work the next morning, Leigh found herself even more queasy at the thought of having to pretend to be in love with Ruiz when he was actually with her. Somehow she could just imagine those dark brows jerking up icily at even the use of his christian name, let alone a few odd endearments and soft glances. She wished wholeheartedly that she had never suggested it, but she had to go on with it now, because it was the only way the deception would really succeed.

When she arrived at the office there was a little moment of awkwardness before answering his buzzer, but she need not have worried. He was just the same as usual, not even mentioning their engagement.

Kerry, however, was an entirely different proposition. Towards the end of the day she invaded Leigh's office and came straight to the point in her usual direct way.

"Did you know that there's a rumour going round that you're going to marry Ruiz Aldoret? It only just reached me, or I'd have tried to put a stop to it earlier." She made an angry little movement. "I'd like to strangle the idiot who started it! Lord knows what he'll say if it gets to his ears."

Leigh looked up at her and a slow, deliberate smile curved her lips. "I started it."

Kerry looked at her blankly. "You started it?"

Leigh nodded. "It's not a rumour. I am going to marry him."

"You're mad!"

"No, I happen to love him."

"Bosh!" Kerry retorted inelegantly. "You're no more in love with him than I am." She looked at her friend with a worried expression and demanded to be told the truth, whereupon she found herself the recipient of the story that Leigh was by now word perfect in, but which, contrary to its effect on everybody else, made not the slightest impression on Kerry. "That's just about the craziest, most transparent nonsense I've ever heard," she stated disgustedly when Leigh had finished. "Now tell me the truth."

"It is the truth," Leigh protested.

"Oh, for heaven's sake! I've known you for too long—and maybe I see things differently from your family."

Leigh shrugged, abruptly beaten. "All right," she admitted a little wearily. "You win. Neither of us are in love. It's a business arrangement from start to finish. He has to be married and return to Mexico in order to inherit the family estates."

Kerry whistled softly. "That's more like it." She shook her head, aware of a feeling of deep dismay. "But why in heaven's name enter into such an arrangement? What about Bruce?"

She did not really need to ask the questions, of course. She could guess something of what had happened.

"Bruce wants to marry Stella," Leigh said quietly, confirming what her friend had been thinking. She found it helped to be able to talk to Kerry about it, quite unaware that Kerry was viciously and fervently wishing that somebody would strangle Stella.

Kerry listened in grim silence to the terse words that explained how Leigh had found out, and the very clipped composure of them told her how deeply Leigh was feeling the hurt of what had happened.

"... so I thought something like this would help them," Leigh finished. "Stella would probably blame herself and still refuse to marry Bruce if she didn't believe I was in love with someone else."

Stella was not ever likely to blame herself for anything, Kerry thought acidly. At that moment she was tempted to burst out with all her suspicions of Stella, but she restrained herself yet again, because she knew it was no good. Leigh would not believe her and it might even break up their friendship, or at least make it strained. So once again she kept silent—then the dismayed consternation increased as she suddenly thought of something else.

"This . . . er . . . business marriage?" She slanted her friend a hesitant side glance. "It doesn't have to provide a heir for the estates too, does it?"

Leigh felt herself blushing furiously. "Of course not," she denied hastily, although she could not help but feel that an heir was exactly what that provision had meant, but if Ruiz chose to close his eyes to the unwritten part of the conditions of inheritance, it was not her part to open them—and certainly not her desire. She could not think of anything more horrible than to give herself to somebody so inhuman as Ruiz Aldoret. If that had been part of the condition, she would not have agreed under any circumstances. There would have to be some other way found to help Stella and Bruce.

"Do you think anyone else will guess the real reason for the engagement?" she asked a little anxiously.

Kerry shook her head vehemently. "Good lord, no! I wasn't sure myself," she lied valiantly. "The others will probably believe you've been in love with him all the time—but how are you going to get over the fact that it's only a business arrangement? If His Lordship goes around with his usual air of remote detachment your mother for one is going to smell a rat," she pointed out inelegantly, a pronouncement with which Leigh agreed, because Margaret Dermot had an uncomfortably acute perception.

Leigh smiled slightly. "I asked him if he would mind pretending to be in love with me," she said blandly, rather enjoying the effect that little bit of information would have on Kerry.

Kerry did not disappoint her. For one moment her mouth actually hung open. "You did *what?*" She blinked slightly and shook her head. "All right, you needn't repeat it. I heard you the first time. I just couldn't believe it." She grinned and asked with frank, delighted curiosity, forgetting Stella for the moment, "How long did the icy silence last, and in what manner did His Nibs blast when he came out of his own stunned shock?"

"He agreed," Leigh told her calmly.

"He did what?" Kerry looked at her blankly again, shaking her head. "I don't believe you."

Leigh shrugged. "Just wait and see."

Suddenly Kerry grinned. "I can't wait." She chuckled, again diverted from concern and dismay at Stella's mischief-making by the novel and intriguing thought of Ruiz Aldoret pretending to be in love with his secretary. "I'd like to be peeping through the keyhole when the man sweeps you up into a passionate embrace," she finished provocatively, with a frankly teasing grin.

Surprisingly enough Leigh flushed at that and, at another time and under different circumstances, Kerry might have given her a speculative glance.

"I hardly think that's likely," Leigh denied hastily. "Only real extroverts make love in public, and it won't be necessary when we're alone."

Kerry shook her head. "I still can't imagine him even pretending to be in love with anyone—although he shouldn't be the walking iceberg he is, considering that he's half Spanish," she added musingly. She looked up then and made herself grin impishly. "Not that I think you have anything to worry about there. I can't imagine him reverting to type, or anything like that, although you can't tell what his native country may do to him."

Leigh gave her a dry glance and forbore to comment on the altogether absurd idea of Ruiz Aldoret breaking any platonic bargain. She still had doubts that he would even be able to successfully carry out the little deception necessary in public.

Unobserved, Kerry gave her a little side glance, wondering how this horrible tangle would work out. She wanted to tell Leigh not to rush things, to defer this cold-blooded marriage as long as she possibly could, because she was quite sure that Stella herself would bring about another change in the situation fairly soon. She would have staked a lot on her belief that Stella was not in the least in love with Bruce and had merely been alleviating boredom in taking him away from her sister. Her real intention had probably been to indulge in a tender renunciation scene with Bruce—which undoubtedly had happened before she took off for London—whereupon nothing more would have been heard of the matter if Leigh could have patched up her fiancé's supposedly broken heart, without knowing anything about it, of course. It was just a game to Stella, and no doubt Leigh had quite upset things by coming in unobserved. Stella would not be in the least pleased to find Bruce chasing after her with no engagement tying him to Leigh any longer. She was going to have some heavy explaining to do, because Bruce Jermyn was the last man she would want to marry, and with no Leigh between them now she somehow had to get rid of him. When my lady Stella at last decided to get married she would no doubt pick somebody with plenty of money, so that she could have all the comfort and luxury she desired without having to work for it all the time. Fame was all very well, but Stella was lazy at heart. She could only hope that Stella herself would cause further developments before things went too far with Ruiz Aldoret. If Bruce did want to come back to Leigh, surely Ruiz Aldoret would not hold her to that ridiculous business arrangement?

CHAPTER 5

KORVESTON was a town that had grown suddenly and quickly, but not so quickly that its council planners had lost track and let it develop as a hotch-potch of haphazard buildings. Some of the older inhabitants did wonder occasionally how it had so suddenly changed from a sleepy little market town into a thriving semi-metropolis. The old town still existed, on the other side of the river—which was still as sleepy and meandering as it had always been—but facing it, with the old and new again in evidence, this time in the shape of the old wooden bridge and the modern steel structure, were the tall buildings of the new town centre, with its luxury flats as well as its office buildings, its smart shops and large departmental stores. All around it, of course, were the usual suburbs, with their neat little streets of houses, but on the other side of the river, further out, were the older suburbs, still retaining their rural, tranquil air. Some of them were even like detached, independent little villages, even to the traditional village gossip.

Korveston Heights was one of the latter, regarding modern Korveston somewhat in the light of a precocious child that had sprung up while its mother's back was turned. It was here, on top of one of the highest hills, known throughout the whole of the Heights, that the Dermot house, with its quaint name of Jingletop, was built. It was a friendly house, constructed of weathered grey stone and rambling all over the hill top, as if it had grown rather than been planned, standing in its own somewhat overgrown grounds.

In the kitchen Margaret was washing up the breakfast things with the assistance of her two elder daughters, since it was a Saturday morning and neither of them had to work. They were also helped by the twins, whose contribution was more a good deal of noise and hindrance than actual assistance. In the end they were banished out to the garden, while the other three carried on by themselves, in peace and quiet.

"Things certainly seem to be happening in this family lately," Margaret commented, carefully setting a plate on the draining rack and then turning to smile at them, because she was rather proud of her two attractive daughters. Of course they were nothing like the glorious Stella, but they looked extremely charming standing there, Julie with her copper-fair hair in a long, flying ponytail and Leigh with her lovely bronze hair plaited into two braids this morning and twisted in the nape of her neck, instead of the single coronet she usually wore.

"I'll say they do," Julie agreed. "What with Leigh springing on us that she's going to marry Ruiz Aldoret and then Bruce just about knocking us flat about him and Stella."

"Things certainly haven't been monotonous," Margaret laughed.

The news about Bruce and Stella had been a nine days' wonder that was still going on, but unfortunately they had not yet been able to announce their engagement. Bruce had gone to London to see Stella, only to find the flat locked up and nobody there. He had called at the offices of the film company, only to be met with an obstructive reception. Apparently nobody knew anything about a projected engagement between their leading actress and this unknown, seemingly unimportant man—quite natural, perhaps—and thinking that he was just one of those men who make pests of themselves where film stars are concerned, they had refused to give him her address. All they would tell him was that the final shots of the film she was in were being shot on location, but they would not even tell him where that was. Bruce, irritable and frustrated, had gone back home and tried to find out if the Dermot family knew where he could contact Stella, and of course had to break the news to them of what had happened when Stella had been there, only to find they had no other address either. In the end he was forced to address a letter to her flat and hope that it would be forwarded.

When Kerry heard that Stella had departed on location without hearing that Bruce was free, she had to suppress a sharp retort. Privately she considered that the fates were playing too much on Stella's side lately. She had been hoping that Bruce would be turned down flat by Stella, perhaps the truth coming out in the process, but he had not even been able to see her, and all the time this 'business proposition' that Leigh had agreed to was getting nearer and nearer.

"It's odd about Bruce and Stella," Julie commented. "I never thought she would choose anyone like Bruce." Then she grinned at Leigh with a decidedly wicked glint in her eyes. "As for Ruiz Aldoret, I'll bet he does know how to make love to a girl—whatever you said that day in Ricki's!"

For some reason, even though she could imagine nothing less likely happening to her, Leigh felt a suspicious warmth in her face that told her she must be blushing. Julie's crow of laughter confirmed it.

"That does it!" she chuckled delightedly. "And I'll bet he's not halfhearted about it either . . . probably because of the Spanish in him."

"Julie!" Leigh protested, rather at a loss, but she was saved from any further teasing by the return of the twins who, as always, managed to get underfoot and almost upset a pile of crockery before they were banished to the garden again from whence, a moment later, came a concerted Indian war-whoop which sounded almost rehearsed—and probably was—as they vanished into the fastness of the overgrown orchard. A moss-grown wall constructed of the same grey weathered stone as the house cut off garden and orchard and prevented them seeing what was happening, but by the noise it was quite evident that the Indian braves were again riding into camp for what could either be a pow-wow or a war dance—by the noise, probably the latter!

After the washing up was finished, Julie took a book out into the garden and Leigh changed into an old pair of khaki shorts and a sleeveless white blouse and settled down to do some weeding, while Margaret went round to the front of the house where the family car waited on the gravel drive.

It was not a long drive into the modern part of Korveston and she left the car in the parking lot while she went off to do some shopping. Everything went quite well, until she returned to the car and found that, for some reason best known to itself, the obstinate and self-willed creature refused to start.

She got out of the car and regarded it with a mystified

expression. The parking attendant, who knew her well, came over with an enquiring glance.

"Trouble, Mrs. Dermot?"

At the sound of her name, a man a few yards away abruptly glanced round.

Margaret nodded. "I don't know what's gone wrong with the dratted thing."

"I'll have a look, shall I?"

Up went the bonnet of the car and the man poked and scratched around inside for a while, then finally straightened up, shaking his head.

"Nothing obvious anyway. Looks as if it'll have to go into a garage."

Margaret shrugged philosophically. "Oh well, I'll just have to take the bus home."

"Can I help?" a deep voice enquired, a voice that had a slightly different inflection from others around them, and Margaret turned to find that the tall, dark man who had been standing by his own car, a few yards away, had now come over to them. He had an air of distinction and her observant eyes immediately noted his good clothes, worn with the casual acceptance of someone who was used to such things.

"Bit of trouble with the car, sir," the attendant said, so respectfully that he immediately confirmed Margaret's guess. Definitely somebody of importance.

"Then perhaps I could drive Mrs. Dermot home." Briefly the rare smile crossed his face. "I am Ruiz Aldoret."

Margaret felt a swift shock of surprise, then a rush of interest. So this was the unexpected son-in-law Leigh was to present her with!

She thanked him and then, as he made arrangements for her car to be taken away to a garage—with the air of somebody used to giving orders and, what was more, expecting that they would be obeyed—she gave him one of those swift, all-encompassing looks of feminine curiosity, mixed with a mother's anxiety as to what sort of man her daughter had chosen.

The femininity instantly noted and approved the dark attraction of him, the aquiline features and dark eyes, hair gleaming with an intense blue-black sheen in the sunlight, strong white teeth, firm mouth and a chin obstinate almost to the point of ruthlessness. His skin had a slightly sallow look, nothing unhealthy, but as if it needed the touch of a sun stronger than it had known over the past ten years. Her eyes, more experienced and wiser than her daughter's, noticed many things that Leigh would not even have dreamed of.

That firm mouth was deliberately firm, as if years of deep self-control had brought it to that grim line, yet a faint suspicion of incongruous and almost boyish sulkiness had not been entirely erased, nor had that odd curve to his upper lip which Leigh had once thought might have been evidence of strong feelings. She had dismissed the idea instantly as being too ridiculous to even think about, but her mother had quite other ideas. Here was a proud and lonely man who had been very badly hurt at some time in the past, so he had withdrawn into a shell, pretending he was quite beyond ever again being hurt by the vagaries and cruelties of an uncaring world. It was so very obvious to her that the cold repression which overlay his features and even his voice was unnatural that she did not even start to worry about what effect it might have on Leigh. In any case, he was entirely different when he smiled, and that was probably the side of him that Leigh knew.

"I hope our engagement did not come as too much of a shock," Ruiz said, as the long black, luxurious car slid smoothly out of the parking lot.

"Shock?" Margaret shook her head with a laugh. "I honestly don't know how that girl of mine managed to keep it so secret!"

Again she caught a side glimpse of the warm smile that altered his features so much.

"I hope you're not going to hold it against me," he said, and she smiled and shook her head again.

"I'll forgive you," she assured him, wondering how Leigh had ever managed to give her the impression that he was formidable. The man was charming, although possibly he could have another side to him—that firm mouth was a little ruthless. But she knew instinctively that it would not be an unfair ruthlessness. He was a man who could temper firmness with charm.

In that moment she lost the last of her doubts about Leigh's strange and unexpected choice of life partner. Short as the acquaintance was, she felt that Ruiz Aldoret was a man one could depend on and that he would make Leigh happy.

At Jingletop, Leigh's gardening and Julie's reading were disturbed by the return of the twins from the orchard. They raced into the garden, feather-bedecked, streaked again with Julie's lipstick and whooping madly.

"Oh, lord!" Julie gave a mock groan and evaded her brother's headlong rush, resignedly giving up all ideas of reading. "The Apaches are on the warpath again!"

"We make heap big medicine," Tess pronounced solemnly. "Paleface woman our prisoner."

"Oh, is she!" Julie retorted, and prepared to beat a hasty retreat, but the youngest Dermot—by half an hour—gave her a smile which was quite cheekily beguiling, even through the purloined lipstick.

"You will be, won't you?" she coaxed, and Julie nodded weakly. "You too?"

She looked over at Leigh, who exchanged a ruefully amused glance with Julie, but also nodded.

"Have I got to be a prisoner too?"

"No, you climb trees—too good to be a prisoner or a squaw."

"Well, that's something," Leigh thanked them. "I'm glad I'm not to be relegated to the lowly position of a squaw!"

Tom considered the position carefully and decided to change the characters slightly.

"You can be an Indian princess who's been captured by another tribe," he told Julie, and then nodded grandly over at Leigh. "You're the famous chief who's trying to rescue her."

Leigh thanked him gratefully for her elevated position and they thereupon produced a strip of brilliant green material and a chicken feather—procured heaven knows where—and proceeded to bind the vivid band around her head. At this stage Julie began to take an active interest in the proceedings and, before her elder sister could stop her, she pulled the pins out of the long braids, so that they spilled down over either shoulder.

"Ooh!" Tess exclaimed happily. "Now she looks really Indian," and she thrust the chicken feather through the band and stood back to regard her sister with more than just a little satisfaction.

At this point Tom produced a rather battered lipstick from his pocket.

"Oh no, you don't!" Leigh said hastily, but Julie grinned over at her and assured her that the lipstick was not indelible. Apparently she now had a new indelible lipstick and Tom had been allowed to keep the old one.

"Please, Leigh!" Tess urged, turning her entreating smile on her eldest sister. "You'll only look like a squaw without any warpaint."

With a horrible little feeling that she should not have done, Leigh submitted to her sister's ministrations, while Tom disappeared on some mysterious errand of his own. Julie simply leaned back against a gnarled old apple tree with a broad grin on her face, of such a nature that Leigh wondered just what Tess was doing to her with the lipstick.

Before she could become apprehensive enough to call a halt, Tom came back with a large cardboard box, accompanied by Kerry, who looked startled for one moment, then burst into a gale of laughter.

"Is it as bad as that?" Leigh asked ruefully.

Kerry grinned. "You should see yourself!"

"I'm rather glad I can't," Leigh retorted dryly, adding with a side glance at her brother and sister, "I have a horrible suspicion they haven't finished with me yet either!"

Tess and Tom were in a huddle around the large cardboard box which they had placed on the ground. A few mutters of consultation drifted up, while Julie and Kerry exchanged glances of delighted anticipation and Leigh regarded the twins with definite apprehension, which was heightened when they came out of the huddle and she saw that Tess had a piece of bright blue chalk in one grubby paw, but she stood there quite meekly while a colourful blue streak was drawn down her nose and another one across her forehead. As a measure of his appreciation, Tom strapped around his sister's waist, over the khaki shorts, a leather belt from which dangled a hunting knife. From this Leigh knew that she was being highly honoured, since she knew they figured among her brother's most cherished possessions. Finally a cardboard tomahawk was thrust into her hand and the make-up artists stood back to view the finished effect.

"Well?" Tess demanded.

"The final effect is almost unbelievable," Kerry said, her eyes dancing. "I really think it should be recorded for posterity." She glanced at Julie. "Shall I get the camera?"

"No . . ." Leigh started to protest, but instantly the twins broke in, clamouring that the camera be brought immediately. Perceiving that she had no choice, Leigh once more gave in and Kerry, who knew where the camera was kept, went inside to get it.

"We'll have to pose, you know," Tess said importantly. "Over there," she instructed Julie, pointing towards the apple tree.

Julie, looking as if she was thoroughly enjoying herself, submitted to being bound not very expertly to the tree. They used a vast amount of rope—borrowed from the clothes line—but she could have freed herself at any time she chose.

Leigh smiled at the twins, because it was quite easy by now to pretend that she was happy. In a way she really was—while she did not think of Bruce.

"Would you like me to stand over her menacingly?" she asked, and demonstrated, the cardboard tomahawk poised above Julie's fair head.

"Hey, you're supposed to be rescuing me!" Julie protested.

Tess inspected the pose critically. "Not bad—but I think it would be better if you were up the tree."

"Big Chief Monkey-up-a-Tree," Julie murmured *sotto voce*.

"One word out of you and you'll be scalped," Leigh threatened her sister. Julie looked suitably frightened, but then spoilt the effect by an irresistible giggle. "Now what?" Leigh demanded.

"If you could only see yourself! Better still," Julie added gleefully, "if that fiancé of yours could see you!"

"Heaven forbid!" was Leigh's heartfelt retort, and then,

at the request of the youngest Apache brave—also the youngest Dermot—she began to climb the apple tree, quite expertly, with the skill of bygone years, and stretched her slender, graceful body out on one of its lower limbs, right above Julie. One hand clasped the tree for balance, the other brandished the tomahawk. "This do?" she asked her taskmaster down below.

Tess nodded with childish enthusiasm. "Marvellous!"

Kerry meantime had arrived at the house just in time to hear the sound of a car drawing up outside. With the camera in her hand, smiling to herself, she went into the hallway, a spacious place of polished wood, entirely bare except for a pedestal holding a statue of a bronze, dancing figure and a small table against one wall with a vase of flowers on it, believing it was Margaret Dermot returning.

It was Margaret, of course—but Kerry's eyes widened in sheer horror when she saw who was with her.

"Hallo, Kerry," Margaret said with a smile. "I think you already know Mr. Aldoret."

Kerry, swallowing a gulp, admitted that she did. Ruiz of course had met her once or twice in the office, but not taken much notice of her. He now, however, recognised her voice as being one of those in the booth on the day that Leigh had made such a sweeping condemnation of him as a man.

"Where are the girls?" Margaret asked, and Kerry was forced to admit, although most reluctantly, that they were out in the orchard, and just at that moment a most bloodcurdling war-whoop floated up from the direction of the orchard, muted by distance, but quite recognisable for what it was.

Margaret laughed. "Taking photographs of the Indians?" she asked, glancing down at the camera.

"Er . . . yes," Kerry admitted, wondering how on earth she could get a warning to Leigh. "I think I'd better tell Leigh you're back. She's . . . well . . ."

She broke off in desperation as another war-cry came from the orchard, a feminine one this time which, although it might lack something of the chilling quality of the former one, was quite a good effort.

It was also plainly recognisable as being Leigh's voice.

"So that's it," Margaret said with a laugh. "Have they inveigled Leigh into one of their Indian games?"

Kerry nodded. "They've got her . . . dressed up," she warned, with a swift side glance at Ruiz. "Maybe I'd better tell her . . . I mean . . ." She broke off, directing another glance at Leigh's fiancé.

Margaret shook her head, laughing again. "I'm sure Mr. Aldoret won't mind." She smiled at the man, a mischievous little light dancing in her eyes. "It's certainly a sight worth seeing . . . if it's anything like the last time the twins dressed her up."

"It's worse," Kerry admitted miserably, remembering the lipstick and blue chalk.

"Better still," Margaret said happily. She took the camera from Kerry's limp hand. "And I agree that we should have a picture of it."

The whole little episode had taken only a few minutes. At just about the time that Kerry first caught sight of Ruiz Aldoret, Tess and Tom had started to rope Julie to the tree. At about the time that the trio left the house, Leigh was just climbing the tree. Consequently they arrived in the orchard at the perfect moment—and Ruiz Aldoret was greeted with the most startling sight of his life.

Roped inexpertly but enthusiastically to a gnarled old apple tree was a pretty, fair-haired girl, her long switch of hair blowing in the wind and an expression on her face that struggled between pretended fear and almost uncontrollable laughter. From a couple of bushes at the foot of the tree, a few feet from it, two comically painted faces peered and two small, sturdy feather-decked figures crouched in ambush. But it was the fourth member of the Dermot family that brought an expression of startled surprise to his face.

Stretched out along the bough of the tree, her titian hair hanging down in two thick, gleaming braids, her face daubed with streaks of lipstick and blue chalk, was his efficient, impersonal secretary.

Then the click of the camera sounded and Leigh looked round. Sheer horror immediately dilated her eyes and she wished frantically that she could sink into the tree, like some mythical wood dryad. As if she could not believe anything like this could possibly happen to her, she stared down, completely horrified, into the startled, but undeniably amused, black eyes of Ruiz Aldoret.

As he came nearer to the tree she moved, with the idea of escaping somehow, even if she had to climb higher and hide herself among the leaves, but her confused, embarrassed movements caused her to lose her normally excellent balance. Her face crimson under the warpaint, she tried to regain her balance by clutching at the tree with the hand that still held the absurd cardboard tomahawk, which of course did not help at all—then tumbled straight down into his arms.

For just one second she remained there, rigid with shock, then she tore herself free with an inarticulate murmur and ran for her life, not stopping until she reached the sanctuary of her own room. There, for the first time, she saw exactly what she looked like.

The khaki shorts and blouse were old to begin with. Both had on them streaks of earth where she had been gardening earlier and also a few spots of green paint from when she had once helped to paint the garage. Across both cheeks were three wide bands of brilliant red lipstick, two blue bands across her forehead and another blue streak down her nose. A large red blob on her chin completed the "Apache" warpaint—the sight of which would probably have scared a real Apache for life. The green band looked exotic confining the gleaming titian braids and above it the chicken feather stuck up at a jaunty angle. The hanging knife sagged at her hip in a most professional manner, and she only then realised that she also still clutched the cardboard tomahawk, which was painted a vivid red and black.

Altogether she was quite a colourful picture, if hardly the one he was used to being confronted with.

Then she dropped the tomahawk and sat down on the bed, possessed by a childish fit of the giggles, and that was how Kerry found her when she came into the room, having made the excuse downstairs that she would help Leigh "clean up."

Kerry looked worried when she first came in, but started to grin again immediately she caught sight of her friend.

"You're certainly a marvellous spectacle, Madam Geronimo," she commented.

"Kerry, what am I going to do?" Leigh almost wailed. "I can't go down and face him!"

"'Fraid you'll have to," Kerry said. "I'm sorry I couldn't warn you," she added apologetically, "but your mother heard the war-whoops and guessed what was happening. She thought your dear fiancé would enjoy the sight."

"He must be wondering whether he's marrying an Apache." Then Leigh started to laugh again. "I've never seen so much surprise on anyone's face . . . but he did start to laugh!"

She stood up, unbuckling Tom's prized belt and knife, and laid them on the dressing table, removed headband and feather, glancing over at Kerry as she took fresh underclothes from a drawer.

"I'd better start removing the warpaint. Won't be a few minutes," she added as she went through to the bathroom.

When she came back a little later her skin was clear and glowing, the long braids hanging over her shoulders slightly undone through being shrouded in a roughly pushed-on shower cap. When she threw off her dressing gown her friend saw that she was clad in a simple, unadorned slip of white satin and looked far too attractive to be entering into a business marriage, but, as she herself had said, Ruiz Aldoret was the last person to imagine ever becoming anything other than strictly platonic.

She watched Leigh take a familiar black skirt and white blouse from the wardrobe and grinned slightly.

"Shouldn't you be wearing something more feminine? After all, you're not in the office now—and he is supposed to be your best beloved."

Leigh hesitated a moment, then shrugged and replaced the skirt and blouse, reaching instead for a far more feminine dress of soft lime green which was a perfect foil for her hair. Kerry watched with critical appreciation, noting how the dress clung to her friend's slender waist and flared out below, while Leigh herself was thinking that the whole thing was probably quite wasted on Ruiz. He would not notice that she looked any different, or wore anything other than the plain tailored skirts and blouses he was used to seeing her in. It was Bruce she should be dressing for, not the coldly emotionless man awaiting her down below.

Throwing a short plastic cape around her shoulders, she began to brush out the glorious titian hair, which fell in a gleaming flood to her waist, but when she went to rebraid it, Kerry took the brush from her.

"Here, let me do that for you. It'll be quicker."

A short time later, the gleaming coronet fastened around her head, her make-up light and natural, Leigh was ready to go downstairs—and absolutely dreading it. Considering what she had in front of her she considered she was quite justified in dreading it.

How on earth was she going to convince her family that she was in love with a man who meant not one iota to her personally? What was worse, the pretence had to be carried out with a man who was coldly and emotionlessly withdrawn and who always reduced her to a state of distinct unease—like the office girl fearing to be cheeky to the boss, as Julie had said.

The momentary softening he had shown on the morning they first became engaged had long since disappeared and he had been so much his usual self that she wondered how she was going to get through the afternoon, especially with the thought of Madam Geronimo, as Kerry had called her, to live down as well.

"Fingers crossed," Kerry murmured as they went out of the room together. "At least young Tess is out of the way, so that's a help," she added, as the twins' voices drifted through an open window at the head of the stairs, the twins apparently having been banished back to the gardens, with which pronouncement Leigh heartily agreed. Tess had an unfortunate habit of saying just what came into her mind—and quite often it should have been kept there, under ultra-strict censorship.

Her dress made a soft rustling sound as she went downstairs, and she thought again that it should have been Bruce she wore it for, missing him more in that moment than she ever had since she first found out about his love for Stella. It was a hard, sharp pain inside her and she wondered if she was going to be like Janice Martin, for the rest of her life pining for a man she could never have. As Janice had said, time dulled the pain, but the dull ache was always there, waiting in the background for that introspective moment when there was nothing to keep it at bay.

This was the moment that it must not be remembered,

though. She had to force herself to forget, as much as she could ever forget, and concentrate on what she had to do this afternoon. It was going to be hard enough as it was, without longing all the time for the man she really loved, not the one she pretended to love, because she would have to do better than even the most perfect actress. It did not matter so much if a professional actress was not quite up to standard, although it would undoubtedly be bad for her career. People knew it was only pretence from the very beginning, but this pretence of reality had to be preserved every instant. There must be no suspicion that it was other than the truth, because this was life and not the stage or a film.

She crossed the hallway with Kerry at her side, and to a whispered "good luck" from her friend, entered the large lounge, which always looked so comfortable and well lived in. It was kept tidy and spotlessly clean, but it nevertheless had the indefinable something that so clearly proclaimed that it was part of a real home.

Her father had come home from the office in the meantime and joined the family in the lounge. Ruiz appeared to have been chatting to him with easy formality, but he rose to his feet immediately the two girls entered, his dark eyes watching both of them. It was unusual for two redheads to be such close friends, but the bond between them, although unobtrusive, was quite evident to him, even at this early stage of watching them together.

Then he happened to catch Kerry's glance and saw that her eyes frankly danced, although her expression was quite grave. It did not need words of any kind to tell him that Kerry was in her friend's confidence and, like Leigh, apparently did not have much confidence in his ability to continue the farce. By her expression she was divided between concern for Leigh and amusement at the thought of him playing such a role. He had quite a vivid memory of certain opinions voiced in a café booth.

Leigh, on the other hand, hardly dared to look at him, but she did notice, on first entering and seeing him talking to her parents, that he had rather a charming manner when he chose to show it. He was also quite extraordinarily attractive.

Since she must make some sort of effort, she somehow achieved a rather shaky smile, to find it returned in a way that sent a little shock of surprise rippling through her—and it must be admitted that it was a pleasant surprise, even faintly disturbing. She had never imagined that a smile could make so much difference. Or had she? There had been that occasion in the office—but there was something even more different about this smile. In some strange way it even made the breath catch in her throat, and she had an odd idea that he could actually be dangerous to a woman's peace of mind with that dark attraction of his and the magnetism that suddenly came into being when he smiled like that.

"Good afternoon, darling," he said urbanely, while she was still recovering from the unexpected shock of that smile, bringing out the endearment as if he had been using it for years. Probably he used it because he did not even know her Christian name, she thought in some amusement. She was quite sure he had never once thought of her other than as Miss Dermot.

Then, to further confound her, as she took the slim, long-fingered hand he held out to her, he drew her nearer and put a lightly possessive arm about her shoulders, as if it was quite natural for him to do so.

"Perhaps you could introduce me to the lady I met in the orchard a little earlier," he added, bringing a roar of laughter from the family.

"Please let her be forgotten," Leigh pleaded, trying to get used to the feel of his arm about her shoulders.

Margaret laughed and shook her head. "Oh no, we have a beautiful snapshot. I'm going to give a copy of it to your fiancé."

"Thank you, I should appreciate that," Ruiz responded. "I can produce it if she tries to act too dignified at any time!"

He smiled at her again, deliberately, in the same manner, and somehow Leigh forced a confused laugh and, freeing herself, sat down on the couch.

"We've managed to persuade him that he's not marrying an Apache," her mother laughed, "but it took some doing!"

There was more laughter at that, and Leigh was rather glad of it, because it would give one explanation of the confusion and embarrassment her face must be showing. Ruiz had sat down at her side and once again dropped his arm about her shoulders in that same natural, possessive gesture, and she could not for the life of her accept the feel of it with equanimity. She even felt like pinching herself when her eyes fell on the slim, long-fingered hand lying against her waist. What was more she was oddly disturbed at the nearness of him.

Margaret regarded them both with smiling eyes, and if she noticed anything at all restrained in her daughter's attitude it was easily explained by the fact that Leigh never had been one for showing her emotions in public.

As for Ruiz, the ease with which he fell into the part amazed Leigh, and she exchanged a frankly incredulous look with Kerry which said quite plainly, "I didn't think he had it in him," which look was also intercepted by Ruiz himself and might have been the cause of the sudden smile that twitched at the corners of his firm mouth. Apart from surprising her in that respect, she was also pleased and surprised at the easy way in which he fitted in with her family. Nobody seemed to think of his wealth and position, there was not the least sign of an air of strain and he even had an old-world charm that kept her gaze on him in quite involuntary fascination when she managed to get over her first embarrassment at feeling his arm around her.

Some time later, during the course of conversation, the subject of his old home came up.

"Tell us something about your home in Mexico," Margaret requested with a smile over at him. "What is it called... Carastrano, I think Leigh said?"

Ruiz nodded. "That is correct. I have not seen it for ten years now." There was suddenly a faraway look in his dark eyes, an almost sad smile turned his lips, as if he had forgotten everybody in the room and was looking into the buried past.

"You've never forgotten, have you?" Leigh said impulsively, and at that he turned to her, those dark eyes unbelievably soft, and she did not know whether it was all part of the pretence, or whether this time it was a genuine softening, because he was thinking of something that was very important to him.

"No, I've never forgotten," he said just as softly, and for

one brief moment there was something hurt and bitter in the darkness of his eyes, something that gave her the ridiculous impulse to put out her hand to him. "I don't think I ever would have forgotten," he added. There was no need now for him to ever try to forget again, because Carastrano would be his. Then he smiled again, and this time she knew it was pretence, because he was smiling at her, that warmly disturbing smile. "We shall go back together . . . and that is far better than going alone."

"When you've finished making love to Leigh," a pert little voice interrupted, "we'd like to hear some more about Mexico."

"Tess!" her mother protested, recognising the voice without even the need to turn and verify the presence of her youngest daughter. She did turn though and could not stop a smile twitching at her lips. Perched on the windowsill and dangling her legs into the room, one of her father's old ties around her head—with the inevitable feather stuck in it—Miss Theresa Dermot was quite an entertaining sight, although not quite so spectacular as her eldest sister had been earlier.

She was about to firmly order her daughter out, when Ruiz spoke, smiling across the room at the thoroughly unrepentant Tess.

"Certainly. What would you like to know?"

Too much, Leigh could have warned him.

Tess gave him a frankly interested glance—for once there was no sign of her twin—and slid off the windowsill to come over and inspect him at closer quarters. Leigh shuddered at the thought of what might come next from her irrepressible youngest sister, but for once, it was not too bad.

"Did your ancestors come over with the Conquistadors?" young Theresa Dermot asked at last.

Ruiz nodded. "Yes, Don Xavier was the founder of our branch of the family. I am supposed to be somewhat like him."

"Oh." Tess gave him that interested, speculative glance again. "What's it like?"

"Carastrano?" He smiled in the way that told Leigh his thoughts had gone back again. "It is big and rambling . . . very old, with flowers all around it. In the inner courtyard there is a fountain that always seems to be playing a song... and there are more flowers, mainly roses, because my mother liked roses more than any other flowers." Momentarily he seemed to come back to them. "She was English, but I never knew her. She died when I was born. My father was killed a few years later."

For a moment Leigh had a horrible suspicion that, as he paused, Tess was contemplating asking him why he had left, to come to live in England, but at that moment her volatile young sister apparently thought of something else.

"Would you like to come to my birthday party?" she asked, as if she was conferring a great favour on him.

Leigh was about to make up some quick excuse for him, but to her amazement Ruiz smiled over at Tess, accepting her invitation with a solemn deference that inwardly delighted her.

"Thank you, Miss Dermot," he accepted, with an amused twinkle in his dark eyes. "I should be honoured to come. Perhaps you will let me know when it's to be held."

Tess promptly told him, very obviously placing him high in her list of adult acquaintances and no doubt highly flattered by the novelty of being addressed as Miss Dermot.

At that moment Leigh caught her fiancé's glance and just for that instant, as their eyes met and smiled, just for that one moment of time, it was not pretence, then, conscious of a most inexplicable shyness, she dropped her glance and changed the subject.

Later, after tea had been brought in and cleared away again, Leigh went out into the hallway with him, which everybody seemed to expect, and to get over the embarrassment of their unnecessary and mistaken tact in keeping out of the way to allow her to say goodbye to him, she brought up the subject of Tess's birthday party.

"Would you rather I stayed away?" he asked bluntly.

Leigh made a quick little gesture, disclaiming any such intention in referring to the invitation.

"No... no, of course not. I just meant that it was hardly something that would appeal to you."

"Perhaps you do not know what will appeal to me?" he countered, so that for one moment she thought he actually did want to come and was not merely being polite.

"I don't," she replied evenly. "That's why I'm giving you the chance to refuse the invitation. I could easily invent a dose of the 'flu for you. Tess's parties can end up more like a hectic romp. She has a party earlier in the afternoon from which all adults are barred, then she has another one with the family, before she goes to bed."

"I see." He looked at her with his expression closed up and inscrutable. "Did your former fiancé attend?" When Leigh nodded he added decisively, as if it was all quite settled, "Then I see no reason why I should refuse your sister's invitation."

Oh well, Leigh thought to herself, he only had himself to blame if he became involved in any of Tess's pranks. However, thinking of a favourite game of her sister's, she had a last effort at warning him what he was in for.

"One of Tess's favourite games is forfeits," she told him. "And she asks the questions so that she can set the forfeits if she catches any of us. On her birthday she's given rather more rein than usual. If it's at all possible we carry out her forfeits, within certain bounds of course. If you're caught you'll be expected to do the same thing."

"I see." He smiled slightly. "What in particular are you afraid of?"

"I don't know—but with Tess anything is possible."

"Then I will try not to be caught by her questions." His glance at her was suddenly critical. "One other thing—this play-acting. You will have to do better, or you yourself will give away the fact that it is pretence."

Leigh flushed. "I'm sorry . . . it's rather hard . . ." she began, but his rather mockingly amused voice prevented her from going any further.

"I'm sure it is, but since it was your own suggestion you can hardly back out at this stage."

Her glance flashed up to his immediately; her chin tilted proudly. "I wasn't thinking of backing out, Mr. Aldoret. I usually start what I finish."

"I'm sure you do," he said softly, then he looked at her with the sardonic, mocking amusement that was beginning to annoy her. "By the way, my name is Ruiz." He pronounced it like "Lewis" except for the change of consonant.

"It will seem rather strange if you keep up a formal mode of address, especially in front of your family."

Leigh nodded, still with that niggling little feeling that she would actually have to force herself to say his name.

"You have my full permission to use it," he said suddenly, again mockingly, just as if he had guessed what she had been thinking. "And there is another thing."

His hand slipped into his pocket and came out with a small black box. Instinctively guessing what it was, she clasped her hands behind her back in a childish gesture she could not control. The giving of a ring was a token of love and a pledge for the future. This ring was only another phase of pretence, the outward sign of something that nobody knew was just an empty bargain, except Kerry of course . . . and Bruce.

The dark brows jerked upwards in quite obvious mocking amusement and one of the thin, strong hands caught her left wrist quite ruthlessly.

"A necessary evil, I am afraid. I quite understand your scruples, but it need not be regarded as a badge of bondage."

Leigh raised her head defiantly, while wondering what the family would think if they could overlook the little scene now taking place . . . Ruiz standing there gripping her wrist quite inescapably with one hand, while in the other he held the tiny box with its lid up to show a deep, dark sapphire ring.

"I wasn't thinking of it like that," she said at last. "It just seemed to be . . . an unnecessary extravagance."

"But normal, I think you will agree. Your family will look to you to be wearing a ring."

"Yes, I suppose so," she agreed, although still reluctantly, and stood there quite unmoving while he slid the ring on to her finger himself, when she had half expected that he would offhandedly give it to her, box and all, and tell her to put it on herself. That would have been more in keeping with the kind of cold-blooded arrangement they had entered into. That did not seem to occur to him, however—or if it did he chose to ignore it in a half mocking intent to treat it as a more conventional engagement ring. Not only that, the ring itself fitted perfectly, as if it had been made specially for her.

"A good omen," he remarked with an enigmatic look in the dark eyes she found so difficult to meet. He did not add how or why it should be a good omen, but, startling her further, bent his dark head and touched thin, firm lips to the palm of her hand. "Also conventional to the giving of an engagement ring," he commented satirically, and Leigh looked anywhere but at his face.

"It's a very beautiful ring," she murmured at last.

"Perhaps I should have said I bought it to match the colour of your eyes," he said, the mockery again evident in his voice.

"I didn't think you even knew what colour they were," Leigh retorted involuntarily.

"No?" His hand tipped up her chin suddenly, so that for one breathless moment she had the crazy thought that he was going to kiss her, but he only smiled with a touch of derision—had he guessed what she had been thinking?—and released her. "I must have known, since they are the exact colour of the ring. At least I did not think that you would have a preference for diamonds," he added, when she would have been quite ready to believe he knew nothing of her preferences, or the colour of her eyes. He really was a most amazing man.

"I do . . . rather like sapphires," she said haltingly. How in heaven's name was he able to disconcert her so much?

"Good." He directed a glance behind them at the closed door into the lounge. "Do you think it is safe for me to go yet—or haven't we allowed enough time to say goodbye?"

Leigh felt the betraying colour rush up to her face again. Really, she thought angrily, anyone would think she was a gauche schoolgirl! What had happened to the cool poise she usually managed to maintain whatever crisis faced her in the office?

"I . . . I think so," she said uncertainly, and then recoiled involuntarily when he suddenly passed one thin, strong hand over her hair, disturbing its smoothness.

"A necessary addition," he explained dryly. "You look far too untouched for a girl who has supposedly been saying goodbye to the man she is in love with."

Again Leigh felt the colour rush up to her face and could

not find a single word to answer him with, especially as she could still feel the touch of that hard mouth against her palm.

"Of course, if you consider the effect is not realistic enough..." She raised her head with unconscious pride. There was no need for so much derision in his voice.

"I'm sure it's... quite realistic enough," and the quiet unconscious pride that was in her voice as well as her expression banished the mocking expression from the eyes of the man who watched her.

"Then it seems it is time for me to say... *adios.*"

Again she had a little shock of surprise and discovery. Where another man would have said goodbye, he said *adios.* Yet it was strangely appropriate at the moment.

"*Adios,*" she repeated, wondering what had made him use the word, because she had never known him to scatter Spanish words through his conversation. Was the thought of returning to Carastrano shattering some veneer? And if so, what was under the veneer?

"Nothing else?"

"*Adios*... Ruiz," she said almost shyly.

When he had gone she stood there thoughtfully, wondering just what to make of him. The cold, remote personality of the office was quite familiar and even this sardonic, mocking stranger was approaching that stage—was he like that in all his dealings with women, when they descended from the purely formal, of course?—but it was the third Ruiz Aldoret, almost completely unknown, who caused her the most surprise. The man who had smiled at her with lazy warmth and whose touch had made her acutely conscious of a strong, personal magnetism she had never known he possessed.

Her eyes were thoughtful as she turned to go back into the lounge, to encounter a smiling glance from her mother.

"I know you're going to ask the inevitable question, so I'll save you the trouble," Margaret told her. "I like him. Very much."

Leigh turned to her father. "And you?"

John Dermot nodded. "A fine man." He shook his head, frowning slightly. "I only wish I could be just as certain that everything will turn out all right for Stella and Bruce."

"Why shouldn't it?" Leigh asked, making sure that her voice sounded just normally curious.

"Well, we haven't said anything before," Margaret said rather deprecatingly, "but we were just a little uncertain when you got engaged to Bruce."

"In what way?"

"I mentioned it once before, when you first broke off with him," her father said gruffly. "He's weak... wants to lean on people."

"I've never noticed it," Leigh remarked.

"It's underneath," Margaret told her. "Something you suspect rather than know for sure. That's why we were so surprised when Stella was supposed to have fallen in love with him."

"Maybe he just made it up," Julie chimed in.

"I should hardly think so," her mother denied instantly.

"He didn't," Leigh said involuntarily, thinking of what she had seen as she silently opened the lounge room door. "I mean, something I heard Stella say..." she added, as they looked at her in enquiry. She could not tell them her real reason for being so certain, of course. "I didn't think anything of it at the time, but it came back to me afterwards."

"It really is odd, when you come to think of it," Julie commented. "I never thought Stella would want to marry someone like Bruce, but maybe it's reaction from all those swooner types she acts with."

Leigh had to smile slightly at that, and she did not at the time wonder why she should be taking these really rather disparaging remarks about Bruce so calmly.

"I suppose he is rather ordinary," she said, "and, as you say, it could be a kind of reaction on Stella's part, but I'm sure everything will turn out all right."

It would turn out all right, Kerry thought grimly—for Stella. Things always turned out right for Stella. Yet she did have one rather peculiar little idea come to her at that moment. By the performance Ruiz Aldoret had put on this afternoon, it was a pity it was not going to be a real wedding. If the man they had seen this afternoon had been the real Ruiz Aldoret and not just an act, she had the feeling that he could have made Leigh far happier than Bruce.

Margaret gave a suddenly mischievous smile that was remarkably like the one possessed by her youngest daughter. "Your Ruiz is quite the grand *caballero*, isn't he?"

Leigh flashed her a surprised glance and then nodded slowly. "Yes, I suppose he is. Somehow I hadn't really noticed it until today. He's... he used to be so cold and withdrawn you tend to forget that he's half Spanish." Only just in time she had stopped herself using the present tense, realising that at the moment he was not supposed to be cold and withdrawn—at least not when he was with her.

Julie grinned, "I'll bet he doesn't let you forget it now!"

It was quite inevitable, remembering that most unexpected dark warmth in his eyes, that a slight flush should rise to her face.

"Well?" Kerry enquired with a dryly amused glance at her. "Does he?"

Their glances met and a tiny smile tugged at Leigh's mouth. "I'm not talking," she countered and, in order to stop the conversation becoming too personal and embarrassing, she at last showed them her ring. Until then, for some reason which she could not fathom herself, she had kept her hand plunged into the pocket of her dress, strangely shy and reluctant to exhibit the beautiful blue jewel that bound her to Ruiz.

Julie gave a cry of startled admiration that was echoed by all of them as they looked at the loveliness of the square-cut sapphire and its two tiny attendant diamonds.

Later that night, while she lay in bed, she found her thoughts going back over the afternoon, remembering every little bit of it as if it had just happened.

The grand *caballero*, her mother had called him. What would he be like at Carastrano? Even more the grand *caballero*? He certainly did seem to have that innate courtesy a lot of the old Spanish families were reputed to possess—but not the other talent that race was also renowned for, she reminded herself in dry amusement.

Or did he? There had been no doubt who found their little deception the easiest—and she remembered the brief moment in the hall when she had wondered if he was going to kiss her. Had it really been imagination, or some mocking whim on his part that he had not allowed himself to give way to?

Then she found herself remembering the thought that had come to her just before he left. *Was* the thought of returning to Carastrano shattering some veneer that had grown over him during the ten years he had spent in England? And if so, what was he really like? The coldly remote man she knew in the office, the mocking stranger—or was there a third Ruiz Aldoret, until today quite unsuspected by her—also quite unknown, except that she knew he could smile with lazy warmth in his dark eyes.

It was only then that she realised that during the time he had been with her she had not once thought about Bruce—and that was the strangest thing of all.

CHAPTER 6

THE following Monday at work no mention was made of Saturday afternoon's little performance, except a sardonic query as to whether everything was all right at home, to which Leigh was able to reply with complete equanimity that "everything was quite all right," whereupon the matter appeared closed and he proceeded to dictate his letters. Later in the day he informed her that he was leaving for Carastrano on Wednesday and expected that he would be away for about a fortnight. Leigh immediately took that to be his way of avoiding Tess's party—for which she did not really blame him, because anybody who was not used to that sort of thing was likely to find it rather trying. He immediately dispelled that idea by informing her that he would be back in time for the party.

That same afternoon Bruce came round with some reports for Ruiz, as he had when she had first met him. Leigh steeled herself to control the familiar clutch at her heart, but for once the magic was missing. Natural, perhaps, she told herself. After all, the magic had been shattered the night she came home and found Stella in his arms.

It did not occur to her that the pain of memory of that night was not quite so sharp, and if it had she might merely have remembered Janice saying that time dulls everything given enough opportunity.

"Have you heard from Stella yet?" she asked, and thought how odd it was that she could get the question out without the least tremor in her voice.

"No," he said almost gloomily. "Apparently my letter hasn't caught up with her yet."

"Don't worry," Leigh said reassuringly. "It will—and then she'll get in touch with you straight away." She shook her head. "I'm sorry I didn't speak to you the . . . the same day. I shouldn't have left it until I thought I had a reasonable excuse to break off the engagement."

Bruce almost scowled at that, but for a different reason from the one she at first thought was causing it.

"I don't like what you're doing. Do you really have to marry him?"

Leigh shrugged. "I thought we'd gone into that before. It will make things easier for Stella and it's not going to harm me. In any case," she added, trying to joke about it, "I'm getting a few months' holiday in Mexico for free."

"I hope it doesn't harm you," he said just a little grimly. "Leigh, don't you realise..."

"You know what Ruiz Aldoret is like," she interrupted quietly. "I haven't the slightest doubt that he'll keep to the arrangement. Whatever you may think when you see us together, it's only an act. He hasn't really changed. Underneath he's still as cold and emotionless as he always was."

But had he really not changed? That was something she could not quite answer herself.

"Perhaps," Bruce agreed reluctantly, "but I still don't like it." Whether he liked it or not, there was still nothing he could do about it. She had chosen the way out and she refused to change it.

"In any case," she added, "when I entered into the arrangement I promised I wouldn't back out at the last moment. He has only a certain time to carry out the conditions of the will, and if I left him flat, he would have to start all over again."

"There would still be plenty of time for him to find someone else."

"Perhaps—but there's no necessity for him to do so." She gave him a direct glance. "Besides, how do you think Stella would take it if I broke the engagement to Ruiz?"

"It's got to be broken some time... at least the marriage has."

Leigh shrugged. "That will be in some months' time, and plenty of marriages break up after only three or four months. And don't forget, I've got a perfectly valid excuse. Ruiz grew up against a distinctly Latin background, and although he has lived ten years in England it would be quite understandable if when he returned to Mexico all those old ideas revived and caused incompatibility. Mexico has a strong Spanish heritage and they have ideas about the dependence of women. I'm strongly independent. Of course I hate deceiving the family and making a mockery of marriage, but..." she broke off with another shrug, as if to say that was the only way it could be.

"I still don't like it," Bruce muttered. "And in any case, I can't understand your family being taken in so easily. I wasn't."

"It was an accident that you found out, I didn't mean you to do so. As for the family—don't be so conceited. There are other fish in the ocean, and they think I've found one."

He flushed in embarrassment. "I didn't mean it like that."

"I was only joking," Leigh said quickly. "I didn't mean you to take it like that either."

"I still don't like it," he muttered, floundering in embarrassment again.

"I don't either," Leigh told him quietly. "But I'm going through with it. If it had been any other girl I would just have broken off the engagement, but as it's Stella, I intend to do everything possible to make things come right. Let's leave it at that, shall we?" And there it was left.

The day of Tess's birthday party came nearer. Ruiz was still away and she had let everyone think that he had gone to Carastrano to see how the property was, in case any alterations were necessary before they went out there together. He had not really said anything like that—in fact he had not told her anything at all of why he was going to Carastrano, but that explanation sounded good enough if anyone happened to ask her.

The party day itself arrived, still with no word from Ruiz that he would be back in time. Indeed, even on the previous evening he had not returned to England. When anybody mentioned it, Leigh shrugged casually.

"I expect he'll arrive back at the last moment."

There were no comments on the fact that she did not receive letters from him at home because she allowed them to believe that she received letters in the office. True, letters did arrive at the office, but they were purely business epistles. Nevertheless, even though she was not sure that he would arrive, she dressed as carefully as any girl was supposed to when expecting her fiancé. This time she wore a dark sapphire blue dress that was almost the colour of the ring he had given her, a colour which flattered her hair and brought out the lustrous blue of her eyes.

When she came downstairs into the hallway, Julie gave a grin and then pursed her lips up into a wolf whistle.

"No wonder he decided he couldn't go back to Mexico without you!" she murmured cheekily.

Leigh made a mock gesture of threatening to slit her throat and Julie laughed and went into the lounge.

When arrangements for the party had first begun, some time ago, it was Bruce she had expected to be at her side, but instead he could not be there and it would be Ruiz Aldoret who would play the part of the adoring fiancé.

Those last two words sounded distinctly odd and gave her both qualms of uneasiness and also amusement, the amusement because only a short time ago she could not have imagined him having the least idea of how to play such a part—and the uneasiness because she also would have to play the part of the 'adoring fiancée.'

Tess, already having had her afternoon children's party, should have been tired and ready for bed, but of course things like that were too much to be expected of Miss Theresa Dermot. If anything, she was even brighter than when she had arisen in the morning and at the very height of impudence, even though both she and her twin looked positively unnatural at the moment. Both of them were scrubbed and immaculate, even their wild hair slicked down, but how long that state would last was a matter of opinion.

Everyone referred to it as Tess's party, but it was really for both of them, of course. Tom, pretending to a boyish dislike for fuss and parties, claiming they were girlish, always let it be known that his twin did all the inviting, but he would have been extremely hurt and insulted if he had been left out.

When she entered the room they were both kneeling on the couch, their noses glued to the window, while Margaret was going round tidying a few odds and ends that had been disturbed by their usual tornado entrance into a room.

Tom suddenly let out an excited shout. "Gosh! What a super car!" Cars, as always took preference over everything else.

"It's stopping here too," Tess added.

Both of them had been out in the orchard when Ruiz had arrived and departed before, so consequently they had not seen his car. It was one that well merited interest—long and sleek, a powerful black model just slightly touched with chrome. Definitely expensive, in an unobtrusive way, the same as his clothes. It was things like that that occasionally reminded her that he was an extremely wealthy man. No wonder she received so many envious glances in the office from those who believed the marriage to be a real one. No doubt she would have had cause to believe herself lucky if the marriage had been a real one. And not only because of his money?

"You had better go and let him in, dear," Margaret said tactfully, giving her daughter a chance to greet the man she was supposed to love, without an audience watching.

Leigh flushed, guessing her mother's meaning, and her embarrassment was not helped at all by a grin from Julie. Perhaps it was just as well for her peace of mind that she did not notice the youngest Miss Dermot's sudden look of interest.

As she went out into the hallway, closing the door firmly behind her, Tess wandered over to the french windows leading directly into the back garden.

"Don't get yourself dirty," Margaret told her sternly.

Tess assured her blithely that she would not, slid through the door into the garden and, immediately she was out of sight, doubled back for nefarious purposes of her own, re-entered the house by way of the kitchen and crept stealthily down the passage that led to the hallway.

Leigh, opening the door for the tall, dark man who had just alighted from the expensive, powerful car parked outside that had excited Tom's admiration, felt a slight sense of shock, because he seemed to have changed yet again. The two weeks at Carastrano had deeply tanned his skin, and just that simple change was enough to make the breath catch suddenly in her throat for no reason at all.

"So you did get back in time," she remarked a little confusedly and rather obviously, since if he had not managed to get back in time he would not have been standing there at her side.

"Of course. I said I would be back in time," as if the fact that he had said it at all meant that it would be carried out. Then he added, with that rare, disturbing smile. "You're looking very beautiful this evening."

Leigh drew a quick breath, feeling the warmth rising to her cheeks again, wondering whatever had made him say such a thing without an audience—but there *was* an audience. Although she might not have seen it, the man's quick eyes had caught sight of a small, carrot-topped head peering stealthily around the corner of the passage, where it joined the hallway, and a small face that had an exceedingly expectant look. A small face that should never have been there at all.

Ruiz put his arm around her shoulders as if he would have turned her towards the lounge, and a disappointed voice piped up:

"Aren't you going to kiss her? Bruce always did."

Leigh could cheerfully have slapped her sister at that moment, much as she loved the young wretch, but at least it did explain Ruiz's rather startling behaviour.

She watched the dark brows flick upwards as Tess revealed herself fully, quite fascinated by his easy control of the situation.

"Not with you watching."

"Oh." Tess seemed to think that was reasonable enough. "I'll go away, then," she added obligingly.

Leigh turned round to make quite sure that the small figure really had gone safely out of sight and hearing, then she glanced back at Ruiz.

"Please don't take any notice of Tess. She's rather apt to come out with disconcerting remarks at any time, and as she knows we're engaged she's . . . well . . ."

She broke off, at a loss, but he finished for her, the sardonic amusement glinting in his eyes.

"She is liable to look for some sign of it?"

Leigh nodded, wondering just what young Tess was up to. It was not like her to sneak around corners watching people, so something must be hatching under that bright head, and she did not like to think too much about what it might be. With Tess anything could happen, especially on her birthday, when she was given more licence than at any other time.

A battery of five pairs of eyes fastened on them the moment they entered, Tess having returned there when she was disappointed in not being supplied with a love scene.

Margaret smiled and held out her hand when he entered. "So you decided to brave it. We always say anybody who survives one of Tess's parties has received training to survive just about anything, including atomic bombs."

Ruiz laughed. "Then that sounds a valuable ability to acquire."

Julie greeted him a little more soberly than was her normal manner, but her bubbling spirits would not allow her to remain embarrassed or overawed for too long by the fact that her sister was engaged to the owner of Merediths, and after a time she became more at ease with him than was Leigh herself. Tom, of course, still had his nose glued to the window in silent admiration of the shining monster parked outside. About all the attention he spared Ruiz was one brief glance when he first entered, which was not really surprising. Even Stella's homecoming had apparently had little effect on him. She was just another member of the family to him, however famous she might be. It seemed that Ruiz was going to be treated in the same manner.

Tess, on the other hand, for some reason best known to herself—and Leigh sincerely hoped that she kept it to herself—continued to regard her sister and Ruiz with decided interest and speculation. Knowing that young lady rather well, Leigh hoped fervently that nothing too awful was hatching under the carroty mop that was already beginning to lose its unnatural slicked-down look. Leigh would not have cared if her young sister's hair actually stood on end—it was that speculative look that worried her. Tom was really no trouble at all. He was not given to making the same sort of remarks his twin specialised in and, in any case, the car outside kept distracting him. The only thing to be feared from him was that he might ask to be taken for a ride in it.

After a moment Ruiz produced a package that diverted both twins, entrancing them with a pair of real Indian moccasins that he had had made for them while he was away.

Unobserved, Leigh looked up at him with wonder in her eyes. Not only had he intended to get back in time and not disappoint a little boy and girl, but he had actually gone to the trouble of having moccasins specially made for them, somehow gauging very correctly the size of the small feet that would wear them—no doubt remembering an Apache raid he had interrupted when he arrived before.

Did he also remember another 'Apache'? The one who had lain across the bough of an apple tree and tumbled down into his arms?

Suddenly he turned his head and caught her glance on him and his expression told her that he did remember. A rather teasing smile crossed his face, nothing like the mocking smile he had given her in the hall.

"Perhaps I should also have had some made for Madam Geronimo."

"Oh no, please let her die a shameful death," Leigh pleaded, wondering how he had managed to find out Kerry's impish name for the spectacle she had presented. Probably from either Julie or her mother, both of whom had gleefully adopted Kerry's nickname, on his last visit.

"Why?" he asked, still with that smile that had nothing mocking or sardonic about it. "I am sure that she is worthy of being recorded for posterity, as her mother remarked at the time."

"She would much rather have sunk into the tree right out of sight at the time," Leigh admitted ruefully.

"I am glad she did not," he said, so softly that only Leigh heard him. In any case, the others were fully occupied in watching the twins pad around the room in their newly acquired moccasins. "I rather liked what I saw."

"That painted horror?" Leigh almost whispered.

"It was the girl under the paint who mattered," he said as softly. "Do you know what I thought before that?"

Almost hypnotised, Leigh shook her head.

"That my secretary was too perfect to be human, so efficient, always so impeccable—then I met someone entirely different, a girl who was prepared to break her engagement so that her sister could be happy and who, even though she was unhappy herself, would not let anybody guess it and even went to extreme lengths so that nothing should mar her sister's happiness. She could even play childish games with her young brother and sister."

For a long moment Leigh stood there, entranced, her glance held by his, not understanding what was happening to her, then like the bugles of a rescue troop, the doorbell sounded.

She turned towards the hall almost with relief. "This will probably be Kerry. I'll let her in," she added quickly, forestalling her mother's move towards the door.

Out in the hall, she stood for a second as if she was coming out of a daze, then went over to open the door for Kerry, who greeted her with a broad grin.

"So His Lordship's here. How are things going?"

"I can't quite make him out," Leigh told her somewhat hesitantly, remembering his odd comments of a few minutes ago.

"Falling down on his part, is he?" Kerry commented laconically. "We might have known it—though he did put up quite a good show last time," she added, no doubt in the belief that the first time was always the hardest.

"No, nothing like that at all," Leigh shook her head with a rather puzzled smile. "In fact he's doing even better than he did last time."

"Then what's the trouble?"

Leigh shrugged. "I don't know. Maybe it's just my imagination." She could not admit even to Kerry that she was becoming increasingly aware of him as an attractive man.

"Young Tess said anything awful yet?"

Leigh simply held up her crossed fingers and Kerry chuckled, "I'll keep mine crossed for you too."

When they entered the room, Kerry found her own glance going over to the man, trying to discover what was different about him. He had always been attractive, but he seemed more alive now, making women conscious of a subtle magnetism, where before the cold detachment almost inevitably would repel. That dark vitality was now 'just plain dangerous' as she put it to herself. Maybe that was the difference Leigh had sensed and could not quite understand. She might still be in love with Bruce, but Ruiz Aldoret had become the sort of man who always drew a woman's second glance and remained in her thoughts afterwards.

True to Leigh's warning, Tess later in the evening decided that she wanted to play forfeits. Her mind, diverted for a time by the gift of the moccasins, had come back to some idea it had been engrossed with earlier and she made it quite clear that, since this was her birthday, she expected them to carry out whatever forfeits she set if she happened to catch any of them.

"Within reason," her mother warned sternly, and on that note the game began.

With a satisfied air, Tess placed a large cushion in the middle of the floor and proceeded to settle her small person comfortably on it, looking like a flameheaded gnome—with equally mischievous propensities.

"We'll start with you," she said to Ruiz. "I don't suppose you've ever played it before, so I'll tell you what happens. I'll ask you some questions and if you can't answer one, or I catch you making a slip, you have to pay a forfeit."

He nodded. "Very well," adding with a smile, "but do not be too hard on me."

"We'll start off with an easy one," Tess agreed obligingly. "How old are you?" She hadn't the least hesitation in asking personal questions that some people might desire to keep secret.

"Thirty-four," he answered.

"Where were you born?"

"At Carastrano."

So far so good, Leigh thought, and started to uncross her fingers.

"Have you been engaged before?"

Everyone knew that Leigh had been engaged once before, so Tess saw no reason why he should be reluctant to own up if he also had another engagement to his credit, or discredit, whichever word was applicable.

Ruiz stiffened and hesitated for a moment, but at last he nodded slowly. "Yes, I have been engaged before."

Leigh gave him a quick glance, but his expression told her nothing. So there was something in his past, she told herself, something that might have caused that hard shell to grow around him.

"How old is Leigh?" Tess shot at him, and he immediately looked blank.

Leigh began making frantic signs with her fingers. She knew from experience just what Tess's forfeits could lead to.

Tess forestalled her. "Oh, no you don't!" she said with a reproving glance at her sister's suddenly stilled hands, then she turned her attention back to Ruiz. "So you don't even know how old your fiancé is. For your information, she's twenty-five." She nodded to herself with a satisfied air that confirmed Leigh's suspicions that something pretty dreadful was being saved up. "I'll save your forfeit until later," again confirming Leigh's private opinion. "Now, Leigh . . ."

Leigh watched her answers carefully, knowing that if she could last out the time limit set for Tess's questions, she would be safe enough. Her real danger though would be in actual lack of knowledge, such as Ruiz's ignorance of her age had been. Ruiz, however, would not be likely to point out any mistakes concerning him if she did make any.

Tess fired her questions quickly, hoping to confuse her sister. "How long have you worked at the factory?"

"Three years."

"Where did you work before then?"

"Jenson Associates."

"And before then?"

"Went to training college."

Tess knew all those answers quite well and she only shot them at her sister, wily minx that she was, in the hope that Leigh would be lulled into a false sense of security. Her next question was the trap.

"Has any other man ever kissed you except Bruce?"

"No," Leigh replied with perfect truth—and then realised what she had said. The question had been one that only Tess would have asked—and should certainly never have left that demoniac little tongue in the first place—but her own answer had made it worse. From the point of view of everyone there it was a blatant untruth. She could have bitten out her tongue the moment the words left her lips, because, as her fiancé, Ruiz would most certainly have been supposed to have kissed her. "I meant yes," she amended, and Tess gave her a smugly complacent look, denoting quite plainly that she knew she had won.

"Doesn't matter what you meant, it's what you said that counts. I was hoping I'd be able to catch you." There was a pregnant little pause and Leigh braced herself for what was coming. It just could not be easy, knowing Tess. "I suppose you know that I'm writing a book," Tess announced importantly. Since all the family had been confronted with ample evidence in the form of numerous sheets of paper lying around covered with her untidy scrawl, nobody evidenced much surprise. "I'm having some difficulty with the love scenes, though," the amazing ten-year-old announced—and Leigh's heart took on the weight of lead and sank with a thud. She did not even need intuition to tell her what was coming next. "I thought perhaps you wouldn't mind demonstrating," Tess finished, looking hopefully from her sister to Ruiz.

Leigh sat quite still. Her brain ran around in circles, trying to think of some way out. She could, of course, refuse flatly and she contemplated doing just that, knowing now why Tess had followed her into the hall when Ruiz first arrived.

"I'll do nothing of the sort," she said firmly. "You choose some other forfeit."

"Why should I?" Tess demanded stubbornly. "It's one of the rules of the game."

Leigh could not have looked at Ruiz at that moment even if her life had depended on it, then like a bolt from heaven, the answer came into her mind.

"It wouldn't give you the right idea at all," she said with apparent lightness. "I mean a crowd would . . . well . . ."

"Put you both off your stroke, you mean?" Tess finished for her, with an air of vast worldly experience. "I don't mind. I don't expect it would be too bad."

"You have no idea at all just how bad it would be," Leigh thought grimly, not daring to look at Ruiz himself.

"What's the matter?" Tess asked a little impatiently. "Anyone would think you'd never kissed him before."

And anyone would think right, Leigh could have told her.

"She is shy," Ruiz said blandly, and at that Leigh did chance shooting a quick side glance at him, to find that he looked amused—for the benefit of the family, of course. Beneath the amusement she could sense derision. He had already accused her of being the one to find this pretence difficult to play and, silently, he was repeating the accusation.

She was glad that neither Stella nor Bruce were there or they might start to wonder—Stella at least—if it was anything other than shyness, especially coupled with the unwary remark that nobody but Bruce had ever kissed her—then, with heartfelt relief, she heard her mother sternly rebuke Tess and order her to choose some other forfeit as grown-ups did not like to kiss in public. Grumbling and with a *sotto voce* comment something about people on the screen doing it in public enough times, Tess obeyed.

Thereafter, although the evening proceeded satisfactorily, Leigh was conscious of a shade of worry in her mother's eyes and knew that Margaret was asking herself whether her daughter might have had some other reason for not wishing to kiss the man at her side. When she saw that look, Leigh wished that she could somehow have made herself kiss him, but it had seemed absolutely impossible at the time and, even in retrospect, was still impossible.

As she might have expected, Ruiz himself commented on it later, although he had made no move to help her out at the time.

They were standing in the hallway, the others as usual having tactfully allowed them to say goodnight to each other alone, and immediately she saw those black brows go up in the sardonic amusement that was becoming too familiar, she knew just what was coming.

"Again I am wondering who finds this pretence the harder to play."

Leigh flushed. "It's hard enough to kiss anyone in public," she protested, "let alone anyone who . . . who . . ." She broke off with an embarrassed little shrug.

"Whom you have never kissed before?" he finished for her, and when she nodded, added a little derisively, "Then perhaps if that was remedied it might be a little easier for you should a situation of the same kind occur again."

Before she had quite realised what he meant by that, he took her into his arms and kissed her quite deliberately. Since it was the last thing she expected, it shocked her into complete immobility. A moment later she found her estimation of him undergoing another change. Everything she had said in Ricki's had been quite untrue. Not only had she been wrong in saying that he would not know how to make love to anyone if he tried, the way in which he kissed her proved quite conclusively that it was not the first time he had kissed a woman. He was a man who knew how to make his kisses acceptable, and she was quite indignant with herself that she should find them so when she was in love with Bruce.

When he lifted his head she was surprised to find that she was breathless, and would have been even more surprised could she have seen the expression on her face and known that her lips, parted and tremulous, were unconsciously inviting. Suddenly it seemed to her that his hold tightened, there was something even possessive in it, and because that was quite ridiculous she looked up at him, only to find her glance held, because there was such a peculiar light in the dark eyes that were normally cold and remote. They were not cold now, and again almost before she realised what he intended, he bent his head to kiss her for the second time, but this kiss was very different. Frankly passionate and even sensuous, it sent her senses reeling. There was a moment of shocked realisation that Bruce had never kissed her like this, nor made her feel so shaken to the very depths, then she ceased to think and simply lived.

Five minutes later Margaret came out with Kerry at her side and found Leigh still standing in the middle of the hallway.

"Darling, wake up," she said with a laugh. "You look quite bemused!"

Leigh seemed to start and then a flood of colour washed over her face as she turned to her mother. As if drawn by the laughter in Margaret's voice, Julie appeared behind her.

"Oh, I didn't hear you come out."

Margaret smiled teasingly. "Don't worry, we only just arrived. We heard the car drive away." She touched a finger to her daughter's hot cheek, the teasing smile deepening. "No wonder you didn't want to kiss him with everyone looking on if that's the effect he has on you!"

Leigh gulped something and fled to her room.

For quite a long time that night Leigh lay in bed trying to puzzle out just what had happened. The first time he had kissed her it had been almost impersonal—if a kiss ever could be called impersonal—but the second time something quite unmanageable had seemed to spring to life. Every nerve in her body had seemed steeped in fire and she had never felt so shaken in all her life. That it was Ruiz Aldoret who had made her feel like that made the whole thing even more unaccountable.

Was she really fickle at heart that she could love Bruce and at the same time lose herself completely in another man's kiss? Completely lost and completely bewitched. She did not have the faintest idea what he had said to her when his arms at last released her. There was a faint recollection of seeing him look down into her face with a strangely searching expression; then he had turned with a murmur of something unremembered and gone. It was only when the others had come out into the hallway that some measure of real coherence and sanity had returned to her mind, even though her nerves continued to sing wildly and even now, hours later, she could in imagination still feel his kisses on her lips and relive those moments, so startling and unexpected, when she had found herself carried up to a quite unsuspected paradise.

When she realised that she would have to face Ruiz with the memory of that kiss between them the prospect was almost terrifying, but she need not have worried, because when she did see him it was just as if it had never happened. He called her into the office and dictated letters just as he had for the last three years, but she did not know that after she had gone out again, glad that she had been able to preserve the cool composure he was used to from her, he sat for long moments staring at the door through which she had gone and there was a faint frown drawing the dark brows together.

Later that day she of course ran into Kerry, but although her friend gave her a rather strange glance, she forbore to make any mention of the expression that had been on Leigh's face the night before, although she must have read it just as plainly as had the others.

As for Bruce, she was both pleased and indignant that the pain of losing him should be rapidly fading. Indignant because she had never believed herself to be so lightly in love and pleased because no person would want to go through life yearning for something they could not have... like

Janice. At first she had thought it would be like that for her too, but it seemed that fate had decided otherwise, for which she could only be thankful, although she might at the same time feel a little disgusted with herself, because she had previously been so sure that life would be quite empty without him.

Then, of course, she started to wonder why it should suddenly have happened like that, but oddly enough she did not think about it too much, because there seemed to somehow be a warning of danger at the back of her mind, and whatever comprised that danger was something she did not want to face at the moment.

CHAPTER 7

STELLA, needless to say, was furious when Bruce's letter finally caught up with her. The lovely eyes narrowed and the soft mouth looked quite hard for a moment. She looked vicious and altogether different from the charming beauty that the world knew . . . although some, like Kerry, might suspect what sort of person really lived beneath all that sweetness and charm and the exquisite physical loveliness.

"Damn the stupid fools!" she muttered furiously. Bruce was the last man she wanted to be landed with. She could get rid of him easily enough, but that would entail revealing what she was really like and she was vain enough to want to preserve the outward sweetness that everyone knew. She had no particular feeling for her family, as Kerry had suspected, but their adoration of her was very pleasant and necessary—but why in heaven's name had Leigh chosen that particular moment to break off her engagement? It could not have been more inopportune for her sister. Now Stella had to find a way out that did not damage or lose any of the adulation that was so necessary to her vanity.

To refuse to marry Bruce on the excuse that she could not hurt her sister—the excuse that had sent him away before—was now out of the question, because Leigh did not love Bruce—or did she? Maybe she had suspected something—or that Kerrigan cat might have told her something. Stella was under no illusions about Kerry disliking her.

The more she thought about it, the more she became convinced that that was what had happened. It would be just like the stupid self-sacrificing idiot to make a martyr of herself, but if that was the case where did this . . . what was his name? . . . Ruiz Aldoret come in? Leigh was supposed to have been suffering from something like unrequited love all the time she worked for him, but the more Stella thought about that, the sillier it sounded and the more likely the other became, that Leigh had somehow found out and was putting on a self-sacrificing act to make things easier for her sister. It was more likely that it was the Aldoret man who had been harbouring the hopeless passion all the time and, hearing of Leigh's broken engagement, had caught her on the rebound. Apart from that, Leigh seemed to have done quite well for herself, because the man was rumoured to be exceedingly wealthy.

The only thing to do, she decided, was to visit her family personally and try to sort out what had really happened and, if she could, palm off Bruce on to her sister, where he really belonged, somehow detaching the Aldoret man in the proceedings. Letters were so unsatisfactory for dealing with anything like this.

Consequently it was not many hours later that her sapphire blue roadster drew up outside the old grey stone house where she had grown up. The film company were shooting crowd scenes, so she had easily managed to get away.

Margaret opened the door to her and looked astounded at seeing her famous daughter back already, but her face broke into a delighted smile immediately the first shock had passed.

"Darling, this is a lovely surprise!"

Stella freed herself from her mother's hug and went into the lounge with her, putting on a beautiful pretence of unease and worry, so that Margaret, quite unable to miss the little performance, gave her an anxious frown.

"Is something wrong?"

Stella turned to her mother with an apparently impulsive movement. "It's about Bruce, of course."

Margaret smiled. "Is that what's worrying you?" She laughed with some relief. "You needn't let it cause you the least bit of unease. Leigh is perfectly happy with her Ruiz Aldoret."

"If only I could be sure of it! I'd hate her to marry some horrible little South American she can't stand the sight of, just because of me."

Margaret laughed again. "You wouldn't say that if you'd seen her 'horrible little South American,' as you call him. He's six feet two and I would guarantee he would make even your sophisticated heart go pitter-pat, even if it is wrapped up in Bruce," she added jokingly.

Kerry could have told her that the only person Stella's heart was wrapped up in was Stella Dermot!

"Then everything really is all right?" Stella asked with apparent relief, although inwardly she was seething.

It looked as if her original plan—to tell Bruce that Leigh really was still in love with him and had only become engaged to the Aldoret man to make things easier for them—was going to fall through. That way she could have put on another poignantly beautiful sacrificial act and refused to take any happiness at her sister's expense, sending him back to Leigh without any idea of how near to the truth her scheme would have been.

"Of course everything is all right," Margaret assured her. She glanced round as there were sounds of somebody at the front door. "This is probably Leigh back home from work now. You can speak to her yourself and put your mind at rest once and for all."

The front door closed and there were quick footsteps in the hall.

"I thought I recognised that wonderful drop of car, as Tom calls it," Leigh remarked, as she came smilingly into the room.

"Stella's worrying about Bruce," her mother enlightened her without preamble. "I've told her she has only to talk to you and you'll set the matter straight once and for all. The poor child is making herself ill worrying about a problem that really doesn't exist."

"Doesn't exist?" Leigh glanced at her sister with a faint smile on her lips. "And the problem is in connection with Bruce?"

Stella smiled wanly. She looked as if she had been living through a period of mental agony, and the knowledge that she might have ruined her sister's whole future was depressing her unbearably.

"That's right," she admitted. "You see I honestly can't believe that you were in love with someone else all the time you were pretending to be in love with Bruce."

Margaret chuckled.

"You would believe her if you'd seen her the other night," she said.

"Mother!" Leigh protested swiftly.

"But, darling," Margaret reminded her, "you were standing in the hall for fully five minutes after Mr. Aldoret's car drove away . . . and if you weren't in an absolute daze of happiness then I've yet to see someone who is!"

There was no doubt about it, Margaret was delighted. Leigh had always seemed to her so composed and somehow slightly unnatural in her attitude towards Bruce that the discovery that she wasn't always so composed really gave her pleasure, and she couldn't help teasing Leigh now.

Leigh reacted in a way that surprised herself. She blushed furiously. She could, of course, attempt to deny the implication, but she didn't. After all, if a myth had to be created she might as well get to work on it now, and if it made Stella feel a little less like an out-and-out criminal the sisterly bond between them still survived, and one could never overlook it. Besides, Margaret—who so adored Stella, and was so tremendously proud of her—was so ready to believe that all was well, and Leigh simply didn't have the heart to undeceive her.

She went upstairs to her own room, and she looked at herself long and thoughtfully in her mirror. Had she been in such a noticeable daze the other night, once Ruiz Aldoret had driven away, that a shrewd and discerning woman like her mother had been completely deceived? And was it just a matter of deception? Was there something more to it? Something far, far more!

She turned away somewhat hurriedly from her mirror, unwilling to meet the expression in her own deep blue eyes, unwilling to believe that it was there. If she was so fickle that she could forget Bruce in such a short space of time then she was not the Leigh Dermot she had always supposed herself to be. She was someone utterly different, and as new and slightly fascinating to herself as her mother's theory that she was a girl madly in love for the first time in her life!

CHAPTER 8

THUNDER awoke her on her wedding day, and Leigh rolled over in bed and surveyed the dripping world beyond her window with a look of distaste.

There was no romance in this marriage which would join her to a man who was almost a stranger, but she would at least have liked to have had the sun shining for it. It was as if the very elements were reminding her that this would be a sunless marriage, because she was not marrying the man she loved. But within an hour of her opening her eyes to such a depressing scene the thunder had died away into the distance, the sun was shining brilliantly, and she had faced up to the fact that the reason why she was not feeling the loss of Bruce so acutely was because Ruiz Aldoret had been occupying her thoughts far too much lately.

That was as far as she was prepared to go at the moment, though, because there was still that sensation of danger in the background. She did not want to come to any definite conclusions as to why her husband-to-be should occupy so many of her thoughts, did not even want to enquire too closely into the reason why she should feel almost excited as she dressed for a ceremony that was to be held at a register office and would be nothing like any normal marriage.

Julie burst into her room with instructions that she was to have breakfast in bed, and after that, although she was assured that time was passing at the normal rate, things seemed to happen almost on top of each other. It seemed no time at all before she was leaving her bed—hers for the last time!—in her own home, soaking herself in a warm, scented bath, putting the final touches to her toilet and setting out for the register office.

Just before they were due to leave Stella arrived in a wave of perfume and a cloud of sable and kissed her sister affectionately, wishing her all the luck in the world. From the expression on her face she had one or two other things to add, but fortunately for Leigh their father was already waiting in the hall, complete with carnation in his buttonhole and an air of unusual nervousness, and Leigh had no intention of keeping him waiting. To say nothing of running the risk of keeping Ruiz waiting at the register office.

When they arrived the bridegroom was already there, and there was nothing at all about his appearance to indicate that he was filled with any particular emotion. His dark eyes flickered over Leigh in an almost enigmatic fashion, and she wondered what he thought of her wearing white for what was, after all, only a business transaction; but she had not liked to disappoint her parents by being married in anything but the traditional white. Ruiz himself, of course, was as immaculate as ever—tall, dark and quite startlingly attractive. So much so, in fact, that Leigh marvelled at herself for never really appreciating before how vitally and quite devastatingly good-looking he was.

Could she have believed a month ago—say on that day when she had so coolly disillusioned Julie from any romantic interest in him—that one day she would be standing at his side speaking words that would bind her to him in the closest bond between man and woman? She could not have believed it, because it would have been the very last thing she would have expected to happen to her. That day she had been engaged to Bruce and today she was marrying Ruiz Aldoret, a simple little ceremony that was soon over and made her realise that her name was now Leigh Aldoret and the name did not even seem too strange. It had a musical little sound, as if the names belonged together, even if the people did not.

Leigh Aldoret. She repeated it to herself and then heard the Registrar smilingly remark that the groom might now kiss the bride. Without the least sign of hesitation, Ruiz put his arm around her, tipped up her head with his free hand and bent his dark head to touch a hard mouth against her own in the traditional bridal kiss. There was no leap of fire this time, but she could still find pleasure in it and, suddenly meeting the dark eyes, she felt the warmth of colour rising to her cheeks. Did he guess anything of what she was thinking and feeling?

Stella meantime was conscious of the greatest shock of her

life. That Leigh—Leigh of all people—should be marrying a man like this! A man who was tall, slimly built but with a suggestion of steel-hard strength. Chiselled features were darkly tanned and a well cut, just slightly ruthless mouth had about it an indefinable suggestion of passion, dark hair glinting with the sheen of a raven's wing and an overwhelming magnetism that made a woman instantly conscious of him. Dark eyes that looked down at his wife with a smile in their depths.

His wife!

Leigh had married a man like this. Wealth, position, youth and a magnetic attraction. As well as surprise, Stella also felt . . . envy. She disguised it all through the ceremony, though, and afterwards she laughed up at Ruiz gaily.

"I hope you take good care of my sister, Señor Aldoret."

Deliberately she gave him the Spanish title, a tiny little smile curling her lips and Ruiz looked down at her enigmatically.

"I shall try to do that . . . and also to make her happy."

"Just to be with you will make me happy," Leigh said with a smile. That was for Stella's benefit, but she wondered how much she really meant it. Again that dangerous little instinct told her that there could be too much truth in it.

"Heavens, you both make me feel quite sentimental," Stella said gaily. "I think I shall start crying in a moment!"

She looked far from any tearful state, though, and Kerry, who had been watching her from the moment she first arrived, decided that if she shed any tears they would not be on Leigh's behalf—more probably tears of envy.

She had not missed the narrowing of the beautiful actress's eyes when she had first been introduced to Ruiz and she was not missing any tiny change of expression on Stella's face now.

So Stella had her eyes on this man as well, had she? Kerry thought grimly. Not content with taking one man away from her sister she was flexing those greedy, red-tipped claws in anticipation of a second conquest.

And Ruiz Aldoret? She glanced across at him, but it was impossible to guess what his reaction to Stella might be. That charm of his could be made quite enigmatic when he chose. Probably taken in by her like any other man, she thought disgustedly—and if this was a purely business marriage, what right had he to make Leigh look as she had that night in the hallway, because quite obviously he had been kissing her and it must have been no casual kiss. It probably meant little more to him than just a passing whim. Although, she conceded, he could not have done otherwise on this occasion, after the Registrar's conventional remark.

Love and men! One a nuisance and the other quite unreliable. Any girl with sense would do well to steer clear of both of them—sentiments which would have quite surprised people who thought they knew Miss Rosalyn Kerrigan. She might laugh and joke and even indulge in a few mild flirtations, but she never intended to take any man seriously. Of course she had a reason for it, but that also was something very few people knew about.

Men! More darn nuisance than they were worth. They could tip one's life upside down too easily and be quite casual about it. First Bruce turned bewitched and bemused and started making sheep's eyes at Stella, then Ruiz Aldoret had to make love to Leigh—when he should have been doing nothing of the kind if it was a purely business proposition—and capped it all by being taken in by Stella's beauty just like everyone else.

Blind as bats, the whole lot of them. Couldn't see further than glossy black hair and slanting green eyes . . . couldn't see through the beauty to the sheer rottenness behind it.

After the wedding there was a small, quiet reception, then Leigh was changing into her going-away suit, a neat affair of a very dark green, with Julie fussing around her and Margaret doing her best to keep the tears from spilling down her cheeks.

"Darling, I'll only be going to Mexico, not the moon," Leigh chided. And for not very long at that. Her mother could not know that her eldest daughter expected to be home again fairly soon.

"I know. Anyway, it's traditional to cry at a wedding," Margaret excused herself with a rather watery smile. Her fingers touched her daughter's bright hair in a fleeting, gentle caress. "I hope you'll be happy, darling. He . . . I'm sure Ruiz is a man you can depend on."

"I'm sure of that too," Leigh agreed quietly, and for the first time she had a queer little feeling of disappointment that this marriage was not a real one. He could make a woman happy and she would be able to depend on him.

All the same, when she realised how the time was flying, she had a moment of panic. Soon the time would come when she must leave in the company of her almost unknown husband. Perhaps it was the memory of that fierce, wild kiss or perhaps it was Julie's farewell: "Happy honeymoon" that sent another of those queer little thrills of excitement mixed with apprehension wriggling up her spine.

What would it be like to go on a real honeymoon with him, to be kissed again as he had kissed her that night in the hallway? When she had thought about it afterwards she had decided that it must have been his way of paying her out for those remarks in Ricki's, but that did not alter the fact that he too must have been caught up in that sudden and unexpected enchantment.

For the second time she found herself wishing their marriage was real, but she still would not look behind the inexplicable desire for it to be so, to find out the reason for the wish. Perhaps, subconsciously, she already knew, but did not want to face it.

They did not stay long at the reception, since they had to catch a boat train. During the journey down, Leigh found herself glancing unobtrusively at her husband.

Husband!

It had a strange sound to it, even though she had to admit that it was quite a pleasant sound and had a very attractive man attached to it. Who would have thought even a month ago that the cold, rather repelling man of the office could have changed into somebody who could send a thrill of pleasant excitement through her—and who at the moment had just the tiniest suspicion of a smile on his firm mouth, as if he knew she was looking at him but did not intend to comment on it, so she snuggled down into the mink coat that had been his wedding present, feeling far happier than the circumstances really warranted.

As the soft fur brushed her skin, she smiled faintly to herself. That coat had come near to causing a quarrel between them. It must have cost a small fortune and her protests that, as it was not a normal marriage, there was no reason for such wonderful but far too expensive presents had been overcome by his quite rigid determination that she should have it. On the surface it was a normal wedding, he said, and, as such, it was quite in order that he should give his bride a wedding present—besides which it suited him also that the situation between them should appear like any other marriage. And he had also said—quite quellingly—he could well afford to make the gift. Leigh, finding herself confronted by stubborn determination and cold displeasure, had given in suddenly in the surprised discovery that she did not like quarrelling with him.

From that moment another change in their relationship had come about. She no longer saw the mocking light in his dark eyes and when he laughed it was friendly laughter. Perhaps some woman had once made him believe that expensive presents were sought after and always received with greedy fingers. Now her own reluctance to accept such very valuable gifts might have broken down that old, hidden barrier that had always brought mockery and derision to his really rather attractive mouth.

As they came aboard the ship that was to take them to America, Leigh looked about her with interest. The *Blue Haze* had once been called the millionaire's ship, and secretly she was rather thrilled at the signs of unobtrusive wealth all around her.

Without being a gold-digger or anything like that, she conceded that money, plenty of it, could be very pleasant, and even a few months of being surrounded by luxury like this was going to be rather enjoyable.

It was at that moment that an odd thought occurred to her. She had once remarked to Julie that she would not have exchanged Bruce for the most good-looking millionaire in creation—yet here she was, on the *Blue Haze,* married to a man who was more than just good-looking and, if not actually a millionaire, extremely wealthy. Yet his money really meant very little to her, although as she had thought a moment ago, being quite normal she could take pleasure in the things that money could buy. She could admit at last, though, that it was the man himself who interested her far more than anything or anyone else—far more than he should have done.

When they reached the suite they were to occupy, its sheer luxury made her pause in astonishment, since she had never known that things like that actually existed outside of film sets about luxury liners. They had a private lounge of their own, with two doors leading off it, but when she opened one of the doors she was conscious of a suddenly pounding heart when she saw the two single beds there, then it pounded even more and a queer tremor went through her as she felt Ruiz's hands on her arms, turning her to face him.

"There is another cabin on the other side of the lounge," he said evenly. "I shall use that one." There was just the faintest glimmer of a smile on his firm mouth. "I purposely asked for a large suite."

"Oh." She felt that she should have said something more than that, but for the life of her nothing would come, no casual off-hand remark that would dismiss the idea that she had ever been thinking they would have to share the same cabin. Even the facetious little comment that rose to her lips —that probably the stewardess would expect them to have had a family to occupy the second cabin—died unspoken, because that would have made the situation even worse.

"I should have apologised for kissing you as I did that night at your home," he said suddenly. "Is that what is worrying you? You need not be afraid that I will repeat it."

There was a little pause and then, when she should have let the matter drop, Leigh heard herself ask:

"Was it because of what I said that day in Ricki's?"

"Partly," he admitted. "No man would take those remarks as a compliment, and . . ." there was the faintest glimmer of a smile in his eyes now, "they were very far from being the truth, you know. I am just like any other man, and also half Spanish—" was that meant to be some kind of obscure warning?—"in addition to which you are a very attractive girl. Perhaps that is why I kissed you as I did." The suggestion of a smile grew decidedly more pronounced. "And perhaps you did not mind too much?"

Leigh felt herself colouring and wished she did not feel so much like a gauche schoolgirl. Where on earth had all her poise and self-possession gone? When they had worked together in the office he had never made her feel like this—but in the office they had been very much at a distance from each other. Certainly she had never before been in the position of hearing him ask if she minded him kissing her—and having to reply to such an extremely difficult question. At least, more embarrassing than difficult. She had never even suspected the existence of this disturbing stranger during the years she had worked for him. As he had said, those remarks of hers in Ricki's had been most incorrect.

"Did you?"

She flashed him a quick, upward glance at that and then as quickly dropped her eyes.

"No, not really." After all, it would have been a direct slap in the face to reply otherwise, especially as she had not minded. Not only that, his remark told her that he would have known it to be a lie to reply otherwise and might make him wonder why she did so.

"Thank you," he said quietly. "I am glad you paid me the compliment of being truthful."

Leigh looked up at him frankly. "You would have known it was a lie if I hadn't, wouldn't you?"

He nodded. "Yes, I would have known." Then he bent and lightly brushed her lips with his own, adding teasingly, "Now I break my own assurances," and Leigh found that she did not care in the least how many times he "broke his own assurances."

Heavens! What's the matter with me? she wondered. What's happening? There was a feeling of something inexorable and inevitable closing in around her . . . yet it was in no way frightening. She even became conscious of an odd feeling of disappointment that this marriage would not last.

While the stewardess unpacked for her and Ruiz went to see the Purser, Leigh decided to go up on deck. A short while later Ruiz finished his business and joined her there.

"The ship is due to sail," he said softly, and there was a faraway look in his dark eyes, as if his thoughts had gone way ahead of the ship and he had forgotten the girl at his side, but even while Leigh was thinking that, he moved slightly and smiled down at her, his arm went about her shoulders. Quite involuntarily, she leaned her head back against his shoulder and his arm tightened around her, while they both watched the distance from the dock imperceptibly broadening, like a chasm between the old life and the new, and Leigh tried not to think that the new life was only for a while and that one day she would have to cross the chasm and go back to the old life.

As they entered the large dining room that evening, Leigh looked around her with appreciation and naive enjoyment of a type of luxury she had never known before. They had a small table for two and after dinner they went into the ballroom, which was already open. Even though it was only the first day out, there was already an air of festivity aboard, perhaps because it was a relatively short journey to America and those in the mood to enjoy shipboard frivolity wanted to make the most of it.

People were already dancing and so they joined them on the floor, making the discovery that their steps fitted together exceedingly well and all through the rest of the evening they laughed and talked together quite without embarrassment, even though they had been married only that morning.

Later that night she lay alone in the luxurious cabin and looked across at the empty bed . . . wondering.

A strange wedding night. A few months ago she had thought it would be Bruce with her, but if it had been him there would not have been any luxury suite . . . nor would there have been any loneliness. Was Ruiz also lying in his cabin looking up at the ceiling and feeling lonely—or perhaps he thought of the girl he had once been engaged to marry.

That, of course, roused a new source of speculation in her mind. What had she been like, this girl he had once been engaged to? What had she done to cause the deep hardness she had once thought was essentially a part of him? She knew now that it was not, but the blow that brought it into existence must have been something sharp and painful, something that had managed to strike deep down inside him and leave a bitter and corroding distrust of all women. She had a quiet little sense of satisfaction that the distrust was going now, but she found herself wishing that she could do something to help him, more than the little she had done so far.

Dawn light was breaking before she at last fell asleep, but one of the loveliest things about a luxury liner, she discovered, was that one did not have to be early for breakfast.

Ruiz was in their private lounge when she came out, greeting her with a smile.

"I have ordered breakfast to be brought here."

"Lovely." She sat down in a comfortable armchair. "I feel dreadfully lazy."

He smiled again at that. "What would you be doing if you were still in England?"

"Before all this happened, you mean?" When he nodded she glanced at her watch and chuckled. "Pounding a typewriter and looking forward to morning tea—or listening for an irate bell from a certain gentleman who couldn't find something!"

One dark eyebrow jerked up quizzically. "Was I very trying to work for?"

Leigh smiled teasingly. "Well, on occasion."

"And on those occasions you were tempted to tell me what you thought about me?"

"Oh no, I just ignored your little moods," she told him blandly, and then chuckled at the look which crossed his face.

"You little minx!"

Nobody had ever called her that before and she could not help laughing, since she had always regarded herself as fairly tall and certainly not the petite, mischievous type who were usually labelled minx.

He looked at her curiously. "I can't understand how I never saw through you before," he remarked slowly. "You always seemed like . . ."

"A piece of office furniture?" she enquired as he paused.

"Something like that, I suppose."

"Wasn't that what you wanted? I took my work very seriously . . . determined to be a career girl, until I met Bruce," she said without the slightest tremor in her voice. "I intended to be successful, so I adopted the sort of attitude I thought you would want. If you wanted just another piece of office furniture about you, you could have it."

"It must have taken remarkable self-control," he commented rather dryly. "After old Miss Soames left I was constantly changing my secretaries before I acquired you."

Leigh nodded, her eyes dancing with laughter. "It was rather fun in a way."

The dark eyes narrowed. "Perhaps it was just as well that I did not know what you were really like under that marble exterior."

"Why? Would it have made any difference?"

"I suppose not." He shook his head, as if a little puzzled. "If it had not been for that will, I should never have known what you were really like."

"What made your grandfather make a will like that?" she asked curiously.

A dry glance met her own. "Isn't it rather obvious?" He countered her question with one of his own and Leigh felt herself flushing, belatedly remembering what she had thought herself about the reason for the will. "He wanted an heir for Carastrano." Abruptly he seemed to forget her for a moment, looking down at the thin, strong hands clasped on his knees. "I do not like my actions ordered," he almost snapped. "He had the power to do so once. I would not allow it to happen again."

The black frown she had become used to in the office crossed his features.

"Then you..." she began, but he cut her off almost unconsciously.

"I intended from the beginning to circumvent the conditions he imposed. I am married, so there can now be no obstacle to my inheritance of Carastrano."

"Isn't that...cheating just a little?" Leigh pointed out quietly.

"Cheating?"

She nodded. "Yes. Really you will be inheriting under false pretences." She did not know how she possibly had the temerity to say that, but it was certainly her voice she heard speaking.

He looked at her with a return of the satirical mockery she had met so often in the early days of their strange bargain.

"Are you suggesting that the condition should be carried out to the very end?"

Leigh felt herself flushing again. "I'm not suggesting anything," she made herself answer firmly enough, although she wished she could control other signs of embarrassment. Once started on this particular track, it was hard to leave it. "Perhaps if you had not allowed your grandfather's provision to annoy you, you would have made a normal marriage."

"But perhaps I did not choose to give in to him so entirely."

"Then, when our marriage is dissolved, you just intend to live there for the rest of your life and let Carastrano pass to strangers after your death . . . unless there are other members of the family to inherit?"

"There is nobody else," he said abruptly. He was frowning again, as if the thought of strangers taking possession of Carastrano was not very pleasant. "I suppose I should not have blamed him too much," he said after a moment. "It is the custom in Mexico for marriages to be arranged by the parents. I must have lived in England for too long and forgotten it." The faintest glimmer of a smile lit his eyes. "What do you suggest I do, then?"

Leigh avoided his glance. "I can't tell you what to do—after all, that's something for you alone to decide—but I suppose your grandfather must have loved Carastrano as much as you do, or he would not have made that condition, hoping to make certain that strangers did not inherit." It was a most amazing conversation, and so that he did not get the wrong idea, she added quickly, "When our marriage is finally dissolved I suppose it would be easy enough to arrange more the type of marriage your grandfather had in mind—but this time it would be your own free choice. You wouldn't be marrying to secure an inheritance."

"In other words, I choose myself and make the choice from free will, not in obeying him?"

"Yes."

"A dutiful Spanish girl who would marry me at her family's command." He laughed derisively. "Is that what you suggest I should do?"

"I can't suggest anything." Again she stubbornly refused to give a definite answer, other than commenting generally on the situation. "I had my own reasons for this marriage and . . . and . . ."

"And you have no wish to continue in it yourself," he finished for her.

He stood up, looked at her for a moment with a completely enigmatic expression, then went out with a murmur about being out of cigarettes and going to the shop to get some.

Leigh stood up herself after he had gone, conscious at last that she was gripping her hands together fiercely, so much so that it hurt and she had not noticed the pain until now—perhaps because there had been a different kind of pain when he spoke of contracting a marriage of convenience after their own was dissolved.

CHAPTER 9

FROM New York, where the ship docked, they flew to Mexico City and booked into a hotel. It was small but select, with an air of elegance and unobtrusive luxury, a modern building that was part of Mexico City's link with the present—yet the next morning, as she stood in the streets, with Ruiz at her side, somehow she became acutely conscious of the past.

They stood by the cathedral, looking across the Zocala, which had once been the site of the great Plaza of Tenochtitlan, where the sandals of the Aztecs had trodden its lost walks. Now, twenty feet above and built on the ruins of the ancient *plaza*, the modern city could still breathe whispers of the past.

Ruiz looked at her absorbed face and smiled. "You are interested in the old Aztecs?"

Leigh nodded, without turning to look at him. "I always wanted to come here." She had never dreamed that it would be in these circumstances, though. "Somehow the past seems to be still alive," she added softly. Half turning towards him, she smiled. "Would it sound silly if I said I could close my eyes and really believe I could see them walking by?"

He shook his head. "No. I have often felt the same way myself."

Footsteps whispered through the corridors of time. Aztec chieftains passed them, *quetzal* plumes nodding above their heads, fierce dark eyes glittering; warriors in armour of quilted cotton and black-robed priests holding the cruel obsidian knives that would tear out the living hearts of the sacrificial victims; women clad in costumes of simple cut but richly embroidered, their straight black hair flowing over their shoulders, bound round with garlands of flowers... all the rich pageant of the past.

"Over there," Ruiz said, pointing. "The Presidential Palace is built on the ruins of Montezuma's palace—and heaven alone knows what masterpieces have been buried beneath the Zocala," he added. "They pulled down the old temples for its foundations." He shook his head as if he disagreed with his ancestors' zeal in so completely covering the ancient civilisation with their own. After a moment he turned, motioning her to follow him, showing her where excavations revealed part of the ancient Great Temple's stairway. He went on talking quietly and all the time the past was living and real.

In imagination she could see the Great Temple as it had once been, captives climbing the hundreds of steps to where the priests waited at the summit and chanting attendants sang to the gods they had to placate. Ruiz's hand swept round, pointing out where the great skull rack would have been, the northern canoe basin, a round temple to the wind god, Ehecatl-Quetzlcoatl, the sacrificial stone, a great circular cup used for burning hearts. . . .

He broke off to smile. "It is impossible to pretend that they did not have some very bad customs, but I often find myself thinking that it is a pity so much was lost."

Then he went on to tell her what the Spanish Conquistadors would have found when they first came to Mexico City—then called Tenochtitlan—so long ago. Green gardens and beautiful white buildings, some of which did not at first give evidence of their gruesome use. Set among lakes, with causeways and bridges joining it, canoes crossing the blue surface, it must at first have seemed like something out of a dream. Looming up above the other buildings of the city were the pyramid shapes of the temples, the skull rack with its grisly adornments. If they had come on the days when it was used, they would have seen another circular stone, different both in design and purpose from the great Sacrificial Stone. Here, on ceremonial days, cruel sports were played. A captive, tethered to the stone, would defend himself with a wooden club against an adversary who had the advantage of possessing razor-sharp obsidian for a weapon.

"Usually he was killed," Ruiz said dryly. "An honourable death as he was sacrificed to the sun god, Tonatiuh. Occasionally somebody resisted well enough to win himself a pardon."

"What about the Indians themselves? After the conquest, I mean?"

He shrugged. "They are still here... terribly degraded, unfortunately, but they might have a chance now."

Leigh nodded, already having heard something of the education programme the Mexican government had entered into for the ancient people of the land. The original colonists had converted them to Christianity and lived in equality with them, but sometimes ideals die and for a long time the Indians had existed in slavery. Now, four hundred years later, it seemed the old purpose was being brought back.

"Are there many of them still around?" she asked curiously.

He nodded. "About two-fifths of the population of Mexico are pure-blooded Indians. If you take away the rest, those with a touch of Indian blood, only about a twentieth of the present population would remain."

Leigh gave him a curious look. "Have you any Indian blood?" she asked.

Ruiz smiled. "No, we don't have any Aztec blood." He regarded her teasingly. "Does that disappoint you? Would I be more exciting with Indian blood?"

"Very much," she told him, her eyes dancing. "But I'm willing to accept you without it."

He laughed and turned her in another direction.

"I think you might like to see the museum since you have such a feeling for the past."

Since there was nothing she would have liked better she agreed instantly and, on arriving at the museum, was surprised by the vast amount of relics that had been saved from a varied and bloodthirsty past. After lunch they did a different kind of sightseeing, making their way to Mexico City's modern shops where, in spite of her protests, he insisted on buying anything that took her fancy. In the end, in sheer self-defence, feeling that she was taking altogether too much, she kept silent, but even that did not entirely serve the purpose, since he seemed to have acquired the ability to read her expression.

That evening they dined at a modern restaurant and joined other couples on the surprisingly large dance floor. She had already discovered, on board ship, that he was an excellent dancer and did not seem to be out of practice, although from his previous attitude in the office she did not think he would have attended many social functions. There was a grace and fluidity to his movements she would never have suspected before, but as she told herself so often, he was so completely different from the man she had known in the office that it was not really surprising that she should be finding out new things about him almost every day. Every minute he seemed to be changing more and more, until one day she was quite sure nobody would be able to find in him anything at all of the Ruiz Aldoret who had once owned Merediths. He would be an utter stranger to anyone else, but not to her because, being constantly at his side, she could watch the change taking place.

The next day they joined a dinner party, and although she was shy at first, Leigh soon lost her nervousness when she realised that she could speak understandably enough and could join in the conversation around her. It seemed that although Ruiz might not have communicated with anyone in Carastrano, he had not completely lost touch with many of his friends in Mexico and on his previous visit had renewed old acquaintances. One of them was apparently a popular young actor who had grown up near him and was as lively and audacious as a piece of quicksilver. She had only been in Mexico City for a few days, but she already recognised the name of Ramon Talmonte as being one of their most popular actors.

During the evening she watched Ruiz, listening to his soft voice speaking in Spanish, quickly and fluently. His polished dark head gleamed under the lights just as theirs did and he seemed as if he was no different at all from any of them. He even danced like they did, and these Latins seemed to have grace and rhythm in their every movement when it came to dancing.

She felt a little traitorous about it, but she could not help admitting that she enjoyed dancing with him more than she had with Bruce.

The evening was also momentous as being the first time that her new name did not sound strange to her. It was even rather pleasant to hear herself addressed as Señora Aldoret.

The next day they dined and danced alone and spoke English together, but after hearing him use the Spanish language so much—especially the evening before—the one she had been used to hearing from him all the time they had worked together in the office now seemed strange on his lips and not quite so natural.

"You know, I think I like you speaking Spanish better," she said, and then blushed, realising that it was not really her place to voice any preferences. "I'm sorry," she excused a little confusedly. "I mean I . . ."

Ruiz smiled. "Sometimes I wonder which of the two is my language."

"Haven't you any preference?"

He appeared to consider for a moment, then shrugged. "I don't really know. I like both . . . but I learned to speak Spanish first, of course." He smiled again, a curiously warm smile that sent a queer little tingle through her. "Perhaps I should let you decide for me."

"Well, now that you've come home, you will naturally be speaking Spanish," she said with a return of confusion, knowing that was not quite what he had meant.

After that they danced for a little longer, then retired to their own separate rooms, where Leigh fell asleep to dream an exceedingly peculiar dream. It seemed that Stella suddenly appeared to her and said it was all a mistake and that she did not really want Bruce . . . that her sister could have him back again if she wanted him. That in itself was quite silly, of course—but what really amazed her was the fact that her dream self protested that she did not want Bruce back—protested quite vehemently—and appeared sincere about it.

"I would rather stay as I am," she told Stella, and then Ruiz somehow appeared in the dream and smiled that warm little smile, the smile that had sent a glow through her earlier.

In the morning a garage attendant drove up in a large black car, bought the last time Ruiz was in Mexico City, enabling them to take longer trips. Their first was out on the Calle de Tacuba, following an old causeway to Tlacopan, where Cortes long ago had made a disheartened retreat. The same cypress that had been there when the famous general had wept beneath it was still growing, a living link with the past, and in the main *plaza* of Azcapotzalco, the capital of the ancient Toltec and Tepanec chieftains, a church had been built on the remains of a once impressive platform. On the way back to Mexico City they visited the spot where the Indians had once come to do homage to Tonantzin, the Aztec goddess of motherhood.

At first she was reluctant to indulge her interest in Mexico's past too much, in case it bored him, but when it finally dawned on her that he was receiving as much enjoyment from it as she was, she made no attempt to restrain her interest and smiled to herself when she realised that he was proud to show it to her. He loved this country's past as well as its present . . . and then, of course, there was Carastrano. No wonder he had been willing to do almost anything to gain the heritage that was waiting for him.

After a week of indulging their love of the past, they decided that it was time to continue on to Carastrano, but even then they broke their journey to drive out to Teotihuacan. Here the government had been excavating the once mighty city and the old ruins still seemed to have some breath of grandeur, brooding on ancient glories. Teotihuacan, the first of the sacred temple cities . . . and the greatest, city of the Toltecs, those ancient, mysterious architects and mechanics, skilled in carpentry and agriculture and so many other things. The whole valley of Teotihuacan, three and a half miles long and nearly two miles wide, was paved and the whole area was clustered with the ruins of imposing buildings deserted even before the Spaniards came to Mexico.

More than anything else she had seen, Leigh knew she would always remember Teotihuacan, and she turned round more than once, watching as its pyramids faded slowly from the skyline. After that they turned on to the road that would lead them to Carastrano, still so many miles away.

They stopped for lunch at a fairly large hotel where she saw a fair amount of tourists and heard American accents, but the place where they had dinner and stayed for the night was entirely Spanish, an old colonial type house that had been converted into a restaurant, with a few large, airy rooms above. In the morning, after a light breakfast, they recommenced their drive. They could have gone by train, but as he said that the journey by road was far more interesting she had readily agreed to go by road.

It was about midday that they came to a small village and just outside its boundaries Ruiz slowed the car, turning to her with a smile.

"Would you like to go to a fortune-teller?"

"I'd love to," Leigh replied immediately. "I know you can't believe a word they say, but," she added with a little amused laugh at herself, "they're still fascinating!"

The fortune-teller in this instance was a small wrinkled woman who lived in a hut right on the edge of a lake. She looked at them enigmatically—surely the stock-in-trade of all-fortune tellers—and directed that Leigh was to sit on a small stool outside the hut, sat down herself on the ground, with a large flattish bowl of water before her. Leigh was given a handful of dirt to hold for a moment, then instructed to throw it into the bowl, whereupon the woman peered intently into the bowl for some minutes.

"There has been unhappiness," she said at last, without looking up. "For a time it shall be forgotten, but it must return." She poked mysteriously at some floating grains of dust. "Sadness mists the water." Just as if to prove her wrong, at that moment the sun, hidden momentarily by one of the few clouds in the sky, came out of hiding and sparkled right across the water.

A tiny little smile twitched involuntarily at Leigh's lips—although underneath there was just a faint suspicion of something approaching wonder that the woman could know she had been unhappy. But perhaps there were faint signs of it in her face, and to someone as old as this woman they might be readable.

"You smile," the woman said suddenly, looking up and catching the amusement which Leigh hastily erased. "But there is a dark star in your life, my child, and not until it has set can the sun rise and lasting happiness take its place."

With that she got up abruptly, tipped the water into the lake and went into her hut and shut the door firmly. Ruiz left a few coins on the stool and, his fingers light on Leigh's elbow, steered her back to the car. There he seemed to become aware that she was silent, her expression slightly strained instead of amused.

He turned her to face him, smiling slightly. "You're not taking her seriously, are you?"

"No . . . no, of course not," Leigh said hastily, but she could not help adding, "How did she know I had been unhappy, though?"

"These old ones learn to read signs in the face that others miss—but we shall try to arrange that there is no more unhappiness for you."

Leigh made herself smile, but she could not quite forget the old woman's words, in spite of any amount of self-derision . . . could not help wondering.

What had she meant by there being a dark star in her life—and then, suddenly remembering what they sometimes jokingly called Stella, she gave a little gasp.

Ruiz glanced at her. "What is the matter?"

"Nothing . . . I mean . . ."

"You're not letting her bother you?" He removed one hand from the wheel and caught up her hand, holding it beneath his own as his fingers gripped the wheel. "I should not have taken you to see her."

"It's silly, but I suppose there's something superstitious in all of us . . . and something sometimes strikes a chord," she said a little haltingly, finding the clasp of his fingers comforting.

"Forget her," he ordered.

Leigh endeavoured to obey, but she could not quite forget, not yet anyway. They called Stella their dark star—using it in a proud and affectionate sense, not anything ominous—and although she had caused some unhappiness in her sister's life, it had not been deliberate. She had not been able to help falling in love with Bruce . . . these things just happened.

But what had the old woman meant by saying that not until the dark star had set could lasting happiness come to her?

Towards late afternoon Ruiz stopped the car at the top of a long incline. A little curiously, Leigh followed him when he held the door open and led the way nearer to the edge of the hill.

"Carastrano."

She followed his pointing hand and looked down. The hill fell away in a series of gentle slopes and terraces and when it at last met level ground, set like a jewel in a spreading plain, was a large white building surrounded by a brilliant blaze of colour that she guessed must be flowers. A little distance from it a small township clustered, as if it was a relic from the days when Carastrano had been a miniature and self-contained community.

"It's beautiful," she heard herself say softly, understanding now why he could contract a loveless marriage to retain it.

They returned to the car and Carastrano was lost to sight as they twisted between the low hills to descend. Finally they were sweeping through the township, which looked as if it could have come straight from some old colonial film. There were even men and women around wearing the old traditional dress—and they probably gave more loyalty to the Aldoret family than they did to the government itself.

She darted a swift glance at Ruiz, wondering what he would look like if he dressed like that too and if, at Carastrano, he ever fell back into the old mode of dress. It would suit him far more than conventional modern attire. Then the car was leaving the village behind and closing the last of the distance to Carastrano.

Near at hand the building was even more beautiful. There was no actual drive up to the house, except the road itself, which swept straight up to a high, white wall. Climbing roses peeped over the top of the old stone wall and high metal gates stood open, a half obliterated family crest on their surface. She only had a moment to try to make out what the crest was, then the car was passing through the open gates and drawing to a standstill in a stone-paved patio, with more roses rioting everywhere. Directly in front of them a flight of steps led upwards to a series of Moorish arches. At the top of the steps and behind the sweeping arches, the terrace was paved with tiny blue tiles and in the white wall of the building itself heavy wooden doors stood open.

They walked between the great doors which bore the same worn crest as the metal gates had and then, in a dim, cool hallway a small but very plump woman curtsied to them with old-fashioned deference. Behind her all the rest of the staff were lined up, bowing or curtseying as Ruiz introduced them all in turn, then they were dismissed by plump little Chita Estoril, the housekeeper.

Ruiz ordered coffee to be brought to them, then led the way into a long, low room that looked out over an inner, sunken patio that gave Leigh an immediate desire to explore.

"I'm getting itchy feet," she said to Ruiz over her shoulder, and he smiled.

"I'll take you on a view of inspection after you've had some refreshment. I hope you like it."

"What I've seen so far is absolutely beautiful." So beautiful that already it had started to twine itself around her heart.

They seated themselves in highbacked chairs of some old black wood that shone with continual polishing. The back and seat were padded with leather that was gilded and painted and still brilliant, although it must have been very old. Coffee, when Chita brought it in, was served in hand-painted fragile little cups.

"I feel as if I've stepped back in time."

Ruiz nodded. "Carastrano was built in old colonial times. We have tried to modernise it without in any way spoiling the main appearance."

"You seem to have succeeded." She noted with amusement that he was already speaking as the owner of Carastrano.

When they had finished their coffee, Ruiz rose to his feet. "Now I will take you on the tour of inspection you wanted."

Out in the hallway he turned her towards an archway that led into a corridor that was panelled entirely in glass. This led directly to the south wing, and its apparent panderings to vanity became a little more understandable when it transpired that the whole of the ground floor of the south wing was taken up by a ballroom. On one side of the ballroom long windows opened out into the courtyard and on the other side to a terrace fronted by the marching rows of archways she had seen as they approached Carastrano.

"It's . . . quite impressive," she said a little breathlessly, imagining the beautiful room echoing to music and gaiety.

He smiled and nodded. "We must have a dance to celebrate our homecoming."

Homecoming. Was that what it was to her too?

"I'll take you to meet some of our neighbours," he said, coming out into the courtyard and crossing to the wing directly opposite. In this part of the building were reception rooms and, of course, at the front of the building also more rooms, some large, some small, some exceedingly formal and a few that while they were as beautiful as the rest had that indefinable "lived in" look about them. These apparently were the rooms most used by the Aldoret family.

From there they returned to the hall, their footsteps whispering over the old, fine-grained wood as they crossed to the wide staircase that swept down from above. That stairway must have been centuries old and up its wide, shallow steps must have gone long-dead *caballeros* and their ladies, jewelled combs in dark hair and flowing mantillas. It was strange to realise that she had married a man whose background was so very different from her own, that long ago, in the past, ships from her country and galleons from his had faced each other in war. There were rumours of buccaneering ancestors in her own family, and she wondered suddenly if one of them had ever been on a ship that had engaged one that was perhaps commanded by a long-dead Aldoret. As Ruiz had said, his family had originally come over with the Conquistadors, so they had been over this side of the world when the buccaneers had been plying their trade in the Caribbean.

Now the guns of war had long since died and she came as a bride to this old house with its many memories of the past —a temporary bride. A bride who came to visit and not to stay.

At the top of the stairway there was a three-sided gallery that overlooked the hall and, at each end of the centre part of the gallery, delicate and rather Moorish-looking archways that led into the other wings of the house. The left and centre portions of the gallery were hung with portraits. The right-hand portion and part of the central section was only darkly polished and panelled wood.

Leigh glanced at them and smiled. "Some of your ancestors?"

He glanced down, meeting her smile with one of his own. "Come and meet them."

They went to the beginning of the left section of the gallery and the dark head nodded towards the first portrait in the line.

"Don Xavier Manuel Jose Palea de Aldoret."

Leigh chuckled. "Most impressive!"

He flicked her cheek with light fingers. "Don't be so disrespectful." His hand slipped down to her shoulder and remained there, his arms around her shoulders in the same light suggestion of a caress.

Don Xavier, it seemed, had been the ancestor who came over with the Conquistadors and built Carastrano. They went farther along the gallery and he told her more about the men and women in Carastrano's history. Don Felipe, who had almost ruined the family with gambling . . . Don Renato who had saved Carastrano and Aldoret fortunes by unearthing a hoard of Incan treasure in Peru—and also one of their goldmines—Donna Rosalia, who had entered a convent rather than marry the man of her family's choice when she loved someone else . . . hosts of them, down to a man with a stubborn chin and a thin, ruthless mouth who bore an amazing resemblance to the man at her side, and the final couple, a man and woman who bore very little resemblance to Ruiz, although he informed her that they had been his parents.

It was the man before them who held her attention and interest. "Your . . . grandfather?"

He nodded, with a shade of grimness about his mouth. "Yes, my grandfather."

So that was the man who had forced his grandson into marriage, when Ruiz' every desire had been against such a thing. She looked up into the aquiline, dark features that were so like the man she had married. Possibly like Ruiz in temperament also and that was what had made them clash. That and the broken engagement he had once mentioned? She found herself even more curious about the girl he had once wanted to marry, but it was impossible to ask anything about her. She was a strange bride who knew so little about her husband . . . not even how his parents had died.

"Well?" He must have caught her wondering, curious look.

"I was just realizing how little I know about you," she told him a little hesitantly.

"Which is no doubt unfair," he said, "since I know so much about you."

"Do you?"

He smiled down at her and it seemed, whether it was her imagination or not, that the arm around her shoulders tightened slightly, then his expression grew teasing.

"I know for instance that you have a penchant for climbing trees and wearing feathers in your hair."

"Then aren't you afraid of being scalped?"

"Terrified," smiling. "Some time I must introduce you to some real Indians."

She looked up at him in surprise. "There really are some around here?"

He nodded. "Quite a few of them in the hills, also some at Carastrano who have Indian blood."

They went to the end of the centre portion of the gallery, where a narrow, rather dark corridor led to the north wing. Another corridor ran down the north wing with rooms on either side, some with windows opening to the inner courtyard and those on the other side of the corridor opening on to balconies on the outside of the house. The opposite, southern wing was also the same, he told her. They reached the end of the corridor and turned into the back section of the house, the servants' quarters. There was another staircase leading downstairs, far less imposing than that wide sweeping one at the front, and this section of the house was closed off with heavy doors of carved and polished wood, a relic of less democratic days. Even so, the furnishings were comfortable, if not luxurious, like the other rooms, which were furnished tastefully in a well blended mixture of colonial and modern style.

They turned back to the front of the house, along the centre corridor of the southern wing, over the ballroom. Carastrano was built square, with the centre courtyard completely enclosed. Right at the front, opening off from the extreme ends of the north and south sides of the picture gallery, was a wide corridor at both sides of the hall. Great windows overlooking Carastrano's front courtyard let in a flood of sunlight. This corridor was set with a few antique chairs of carved wood and painted leather. It was here that the first moment of awkwardness arose. The large main apartment, entered by wide double doors with the timeworn Aldoret crest on them, opened off from this corridor—and had been prepared for the master of Carastrano and his bride.

It was a beautiful apartment, with a door leading into its own private bathroom—but pride of place was taken by a large four-poster bed with crimson and gold drapes looped back with tasselled cords at the carved posts and crimson and gold canopy above.

"Oh!"

For the life of her she could not control a tide of colour washing up into her face. She was sure it was by now as crimson as the drapes. Ruiz, on the other hand, seemed more amused than embarrassed.

"I should have thought of this," he said with the amusement still in his voice. "Chita would naturally prepare the main apartment."

Their cases had been put down in the apartment and half unpacked. Apparently the young maid who had been unpacking them had been called away for something—for which Leigh was heartily glad. It would no doubt have caused plenty of comment if the bride's consternation at being expected to share a room with her husband had been witnessed by anyone but the husband.

Ruiz gave her an almost teasing grin. "There is a dressing room, of course."

He crossed the room and pulled aside another of those crimson and gold drapes. She had thought it covered a window, but instead it disclosed a door into a small room that was furnished adequately if not luxuriously.

"Towards the end my grandfather suffered bad health. He had an attendant sleep here."

"Oh, I see." After a moment she gave him a rather hesitant glance. "Won't it make . . . I mean, I suppose the servants will gossip about it."

Gossip they certainly would. That was unavoidable. It had not mattered so much when they stayed in a hotel. There everybody had been strangers, left behind after only a short acquaintance. Here they would be under friendly but extremely curious eyes and for far longer than the time they had stayed in Mexico City. No doubt people would start to wonder if the *padrone* and his wife had quarrelled, which would not be a very good beginning. However, there was nothing that could be done about it Had the room contained two single beds instead of that enormous four-poster she might have found the courage, or temerity, to suggest that they both use the room—appearing cool and practical, of course, just as if it was quite an ordinary solution—but under the circumstances that was quite out of the question.

While he went off to give instructions about the bed in the dressing room being made up, Leigh approached her cases to finish unpacking, but before she had taken more than a single garment out, a young Mexican girl knocked and on being told to enter seemed positively scandalised to see Carastrano's new mistress about to unpack her own clothes. Rather amused, Leigh allowed herself to be more or less banished to the position she was supposed to occupy at Carastrano, humbly accepting that she was now a lady of leisure and position and must act up to it, while Maria settled down to unpack the suitcases with a smile composed jointly of approval and shy admiration mingled with respect.

Leigh went off to have a bath before dressing for dinner and when she came back Maria was waiting to help her dress. Again with inner amusement Leigh submitted to the fact that she was to be waited upon, which was quite novel after her life of independence.

The dress she chose to wear was plain and white, with that simple elegant cut that screamed luxury more than any frills ever did—one of those new trousseau dresses she had bought before leaving England. It was, needless to say, the type of dress she would never have bought herself and had been paid for out of the new bank account opened for her by Ruiz. When they reached Mexico City he had opened another account for her and, having learned the uselessness of arguing with him over the previous account, she had given in without too much trouble, determined not to use too much of it, except for the clothes she would naturally have to buy. It would be expected of her as the wife of a rich man, but she was determined not to take too much. He had already given her the sapphire ring and the wonderful mink coat.

She had just finished dressing and Maria was rebraiding her hair when he came back. He smiled at her in a way that set her pulses hammering—Maria was there, of course, necessitating it—and went off to take his bath. A little later she heard him singing softly to himself and smiled. It seemed that the master of Carastrano was happy tonight, his first day home. It had to be admitted that the lady of Carastrano was very happy too, although at the back of her mind she always had the chilling reminder that this could not last. One day she would have to leave and go back to England, where life would be as it was before—except that she knew now that she would never quite forget the man who had been her husband. Life need not be quite the same, of course—she could have a small business of her own if she wished—since Ruiz had arranged that she would be quite independent in future.

When she was ready to go downstairs she dismissed Maria and called out:

"I'm going to have another look at your picture gallery and do some more exploring."

"Don't get lost!" His voice came back lightly and she laughed and assured him that she would try not to make it necessary to send out a search party.

When they met a little later in the salon she had first been taken to, she was struck once again by the sheer attraction of the man she had once thought almost repelling. He was wearing a tropical dinner suit this time, the dark head held with unconscious pride and the dark eyes smiling at her as she came in.

"No search parties?"

Leigh laughed and shook her head. "It's laid out so well it's hard to get lost." She was quiet a moment, then added sincerely, "It's a beautiful place, Ruiz."

"I'm glad you think so." He seemed more than just a

little pleased that she should like Carastrano so much, in spite of the somewhat conventional words. "Sherry before dinner?"

When she had accepted and held the glass in her hand, he half turned, looking out towards the gardens showing through the arched windows of the terrace.

"I don't think I realised just how much I had missed it until I came back."

"What made you leave?"

The moment the words were out, she wished she could have withdrawn them. The last impression she wished to give was one of trying to pry, especially as he seemed to have veered off before when she commented on how little she knew about him. He did not seem to be offended, though, shrugging with a rather wry expression on his dark face.

"I quarrelled with my grandfather." For a moment she caught a glimmer of the mocking derision that was rarely in evidence nowadays. "About a woman, of course."

"The one you were engaged to?" She made a quick little gesture of apology. "I'm sorry. I shouldn't be prying like this."

"Why shouldn't you?" He shrugged almost carelessly. "Perhaps it is as well that you know. Someone will be sure to tell you in any event."

"I couldn't help being . . . interested." She hesitated over that last word, having been on the point of saying "curious," but that word seemed to really give an impression of prying, so she changed it at the last moment. "Especially after what you said at the twins' party," she added, remembering Tess's blithe and unabashed questions.

He grinned then, almost boyishly. "Your little sister has no scruples about asking questions . . . far less than her pig-tailed sister."

"You weren't annoyed with her?" Leigh asked anxiously.

"No, not really. If I had been, then I would just have refused to answer."

She could just imagine that. He would probably have retreated behind that barrier of cold and aloof withdrawal.

He took her glass from her and put it on the glass-topped cocktail cabinet. "Come and sit down," leading her to a cushioned armchair, while he remained standing himself.

Then he smiled down at her again. "Where would you like me to begin?"

"Well, perhaps..." She broke off, then asked, still rather diffident, "How did your parents die?" Then she nodded quickly, "But you already mentioned that once before."

"Yes," he said as she paused. "While still recovering from the shock of meeting Madam Geronimo," with another flash of that teasing grin. "My mother died when I was born and my father a few years later," he went on, before she could plead for the memory of Madam Geronimo to be allowed to fade into merciful oblivion. "My father was killed in a riding accident."

"And your grandparents brought you up."

He nodded. "I was perhaps a little too much for them. I suppose I was rather... wild." He smiled slightly as he said that and Leigh chuckled.

"I can't imagine you being wild."

"Oh, I think I was," he confessed dryly. "We of Mexico are of Spanish descent and, perhaps as the world claims, we are more readily aroused to emotion than others." He shrugged, no whit perturbed. "It was usual. My... peccadilloes did not worry them, so long as I managed them sensibly." His face hardened. "They objected when I evinced the desire to marry one of them."

"Oh, I see."

"Do you?" He regarded her averted glance with some amusement. "Her name was Mercedes Lastro," he added after a moment. "A dancer in a less than third-rate cabaret." She looked up then and saw that at that particular moment he had an expression of amused derision, but it seemed to be directed against himself. "In spite of my so-called experience, she was just a little more so. It seemed that everybody saw through her except myself. It was insisted that I should not marry her. I decided otherwise and left Carastrano. I knew what it would mean and I was prepared to go through with it. Mercedes, it seemed, was not," he added dryly. "I thought she took the news very well—that we should have nothing from Carastrano."

"And she didn't?" Leigh asked diffidently. The matter began to take on a different aspect now. She had thought previously that he might have been under age and a simple refusal to allow him to marry had been what broke up the marriage.

"She didn't," he agreed, almost amused, although it was still a derisive amusement. "I went out to buy flowers for the wedding. When I returned she was gone. It seemed to be Carastrano and my grandfather's fortune she wished to marry, not Ruiz Aldoret." He shrugged, continuing with a contemptuous gesture of one thin, long-fingered hand. "At that age it seems one takes things too seriously. I still wanted her, but I hated her also and I blamed my grandfather for his refusal to receive her at Carastrano. I would have nothing more to do with anyone here... I even left the country and went to England, to my mother's parents. It seemed there had been some constraint when that marriage was made... they had not wished their daughter to marry a foreigner... but she had gone against their wishes and done so. There was bitterness still and they were glad to receive me, since it seemed a blow against the Aldorets of Carastrano. I was glad of that too, still blaming my grandfather for a lot of what had happened. They took me into Merediths, and you know the rest of what happened," he ended with a shrug.

She nodded. Yes, she knew what had happened. Poor lonely, heart-broken boy, blaming both the girl he had loved and who had betrayed him and the grandfather who had known enough about her to refuse to receive her as the future chatelaine of Carastrano. It was often that one hated someone who tried to act for one's own good and it was possible too that old Don Diego had acted with arrogance and intolerance. There had been a look of stiff-necked pride about the portrait, the sort of intolerant pride that would have been enough to send Ruiz, even loving Carastrano as he did, away from the place and to unknown relatives in England. Probably he had thought never to come back, trying all the time to forget the home he so obviously loved more than anything else in the world, trying also to shut himself away from all emotion because one woman had hurt him. That also had not quite succeeded. Regaining Carastrano had seemed to slough off the restraint of years, and she had seen it happen, without quite knowing that it had happened... or at least she had seen it happen and not quite understood.

Their bargain had first been entered into so cold-bloodedly—it had seemed horrible and repellent—then it had softened slightly at her amazing demand that he should pretend to be in love with her before her family and become even more human—and startling—when he kissed her in the hallway of her home. Now it seemed as if almost all that old cloak of bitterness had gone and he would be ready to start a new life, perhaps fall in love again.

Which was perhaps just what might happen when he called an end to this business marriage of theirs.

She frowned unconsciously at that, wondering why it should cause her so little pleasure. After all, they had both agreed from the very beginning that it was to be only a business marriage, although a few kisses might have sweetened it. It was not for her to want to change it and really she had no idea why she should want to do so.

Or had she? One broken love affair was bad enough. Surely she was not foolish enough to . . .?

A brown finger lightly touched the crease between her brows. "You frown so very deeply. What annoys you? My little story, perhaps?"

"Yes . . . I mean, I felt sorry for you . . . for the way it happened," she said disjointedly.

"You needn't be, *querida.* It all happened long ago. And now . . ." he held out his hand to her, smiling, as a musical gong sounded, "shall we go in to dinner?"

Leigh rose quickly and, although she did not frown outwardly, mentally she was still doing so, trying to pin down just what had caused it. The thought of their marriage ending, when she had known all the time that it must end?

CHAPTER 10

LEIGH glanced up from reading her letter as Ruiz came into the room. "It's from Kerry. Do you remember her?" She smiled slightly. "Another redhead!"

"I remember her very well," he retorted quizzically. "I believe she also was in Ricki's on a certain memorable day and voiced an opinion somewhat like your own."

Leigh flushed slightly, but she laughed at the same time. "You're never going to let me forget that, are you?"

"Perhaps not until I have made you believe otherwise," he said. He seemed to hesitate for a moment, then his hand reached into his pocket and brought out a small jeweller's box. "I remembered you had admired some Aztec ear-rings. I had these made for you."

Leigh opened the box and saw a pair of gold ear-rings that were an exact replica of a pair she had admired in a museum. Her eyes sparkled delightedly and with an impulsive movement she reached up to kiss his cheek, blushing as she realised what she had done, but far from being at all annoyed by the involuntary gesture, Ruiz laughed teasingly.

"The best way there is of saying thank you," he said, the dark eyes dancing with amusement at her confusion. "I think I shall have to buy you more presents."

"You've been too generous already," she told him.

He shook his head, but added, with the teasing light still in his eyes, "With an incentive like that, who would not try to be generous?" and he bent his dark head and kissed her full on the mouth. There was a warm light in his eyes that had been growing steadily during the two months they had been at Carastrano.

Leigh smiled and touched a metal stud on the leather belt he wore. "You're dressed for riding." He did not wear conventional riding attire, as he might have done in England, but dark trousers tucked into short boots, a white silk shirt open at the throat and the wide leather belt that was patterned with silver studs. He was hardly recognisable as the man who had once dictated letters to her at the factory in England.

Ruiz nodded. "Can you stand another lesson?"

"I would love one!"

She went upstairs to change into her own riding costume, the female counterpart of his own—far more thrilling really than conventional riding attire—picked up a wide-brimmed, flat-crowned hat and was ready. When she found Ruiz he was standing in the gallery, thoughtfully looking at the portraits there. There was a scarlet silk scarf knotted about his throat and another of those black flat-crowned and wide-brimmed hats—so characteristic of the country—hanging at his back from a strap around his neck.

His Latin blood had never been so pronounced as it was in that moment, and for a time she stood at the entrance to the side corridor that led to her room, watching him unobserved and wondering if he thought of the long line of Aldorets and himself as the last.

"All those men and women, going right back through the years," she said softly as she came forward, hardly realising that she was speaking aloud. "And you're the last of them."

Soft as the words had been, he heard them, and for a moment his glance held hers, quite unreadable.

"Yes, I am the last of them," he repeated, then abruptly turned towards the stairway. "Shall we leave the past... and take our riding lesson?"

They went down the stairs together and out on to the terrace that ran all round the house, descended steps at the back to an outer courtyard where the stables were built. The little chestnut mare that Leigh had been riding since she arrived at Carastrano greeted her with a whinny of recognition and she gently stroked the satiny neck. While a groom saddled the mare for her, she glanced over to where Ruiz was being nudged by a fierce, proud black horse.

"Not today," she heard him say. "Tomorrow perhaps, Juan," and when he rode at her side from Carastrano this time he was astride a rather excitable grey.

Melida, her own mare, was easy to handle, but in any case she was already a fair rider. The Dermot children in their younger years had always been over at the farm where Kerry had grown up and there had been ponies there for them to share. It was more a case of re-learning not quite forgotten training rather than starting from the beginning.

As they rode, Leigh glanced at him sideways, unobtrusively. The sun was strong and they both wore their hats now and that wide-brimmed hat, set slightly slanting on Ruiz's black head, seemed to accentuate the dark attraction of him. She found that the breath caught in her throat, watching the sunlight strike across the aquiline planes of his face.

When they were a short distance from Carastrano they dismounted and looked down at the building from the summit of a hill. To Leigh it seemed even more beautiful than when she had first seen it, even though she knew its dreaming beauty hid some very modern touches. For instance, that long, low building at the head of a flat stretch of ground was the hangar of a small aircraft and the belt of trees to the sound of Carastrano hid the generating equipment that supplied both them and the little township nearby with electricity. It was like something left behind by another age, yet linked by modern science to the present.

"It looks even more beautiful than when I first saw it." She half turned to smile up at him. "I can understand you being prepared to do anything to get it back."

"Yes," he said quietly. "I would have done anything—even something unpleasant, as I thought a forced marriage would be—but I find that this marriage of ours has been far from unpleasant."

She met his glance for a moment, somehow forcing herself to seem as if it affected her no more than any other pleasant compliment.

"Thank you." She still avoided looking at him, speaking almost casually. "What are you going to do when . . . when the need for our bargain is finished?" He did not answer for a time and she made herself half turn to face him. "Live here alone?"

He put out a hand and turned her fully to face him, meeting her glance a little dryly.

"Are you going to lecture me again?"

Leigh bit her lip and again resorted to the easier course of refusing to meet his glance as she spoke.

"I suppose I was about to... but I shouldn't really. It's none of my business."

"Go ahead," he told her equably. "Perhaps I find your lectures interesting... and maybe even salutory. At any rate," he added dryly, "old Don Diego seems to have a determined advocate."

"It's not quite that," she denied. "I think you're just both plain stubborn, and you're only going against what he wanted because he tried to order you."

"Thank you," he retorted in some dry amusement.

Leigh chanced a glance up at him then, but he did not seem to be annoyed.

"Had you seen him at all... after you left Carastrano, I mean?" she asked, and he nodded.

"Only once."

"Recently?"

"About six months ago."

She nodded, as if that confirmed something she had been thinking. "I think I see now why he made the condition in his will. He probably intended you to have Carastrano in any event, but he was trying to ensure that the line of succession would not be broken. I wouldn't be at all surprised if another and later will would have turned up giving you Carastrano unconditionally if you'd refused to comply with the conditions of the first one," she added sagaciously.

"Why go to all that trouble, then, if he intended me to have Carastrano in any event?"

"I told you—he was trying to make sure that Carastrano did not pass to strangers when you died. When he saw you six months ago he probably received the impression that you would never marry—and really I couldn't blame him," she interposed involuntarily. "I was quite sure myself that you would never marry. You seemed the most cold-blooded creature I'd ever come across."

"Thank you," he said again, even more dryly.

"Don't interrupt," she retorted. "You told me to lecture you." Some peculiar force seemed to be driving her on and she could not stop now. "He wanted you to have Carastrano, but he was probably afraid that you would just come here and take over, living alone, so..." here her voice did falter just slightly, "so that there would be no heir for Carastrano and the name of Aldoret would die out. I think that's why he framed his will as he did . . . not because he was trying to order you around."

There was a long silence and then he half turned away, digging his hands into his pockets as he looked down the hillside at Carastrano.

"So you are of the opinion that I should have refused the condition and waited for this hypothetical later will to turn up?"

"It's too late for that now—and in any case, I could be quite wrong. There might not be any other will."

"But you still think that I am cheating by taking this way out, that I should have arranged the usual marriage of convenience to provide the heir for Carastrano?"

His voice was completely expressionless now, giving her no chance to determine whether he was angry or merely indifferent to what she had said.

"Perhaps you would eventually have fallen in love in the normal way," she suggested tentatively, but he shook his head with quite decisive emphasis.

"I think not." He was still not looking at her, so she could not judge anything of what he was thinking. "It comes then to the final opinion that by taking Carastrano in this way, I am cheating the terms of the will, if not in actual written fact, then in unwritten intention."

"Well, more or less," rather dubiously, realising now how very personal and even out of place her remarks had been.

"Then it is your suggestion," he continued inexorably, "that when all legal finalities are finished and Carastrano is unquestionably mine, the need for our marriage finished, it be dissolved and I enter into the usual marriage of convenience to provide an heir for Carastrano, redeeming my attempt to cheat?"

"Yes."

Leigh kept her eyes fixed firmly on the ground, realising now what an amazing and unconventional conversation it had become.

"But why should all that be necessary?" he continued, and it seemed to her that his voice had changed in some indefinable way. He turned at last and his hands went out to close firmly on her shoulders. "Will you give me an heir for Carastrano, *querida*?" he asked deliberately.

Leigh's head came up with a gasp and her suddenly startled eyes met his in the realisation that she loved him and had done so for quite some time.

CHAPTER 11

THERE was silence for a long moment, while Leigh's mind chaotically tried to fathom out how such a thing had happened to her. It must have been creeping up on her for quite some time and she had not even realised it. Of course it explained so many things, now that she could see what was behind them. The way she had so quickly recovered from thinking herself in love with Bruce . . . the strange yearning that this make-believe marriage should not end and the way she had reacted when he kissed her that evening at her home. That alone should have made her realise what was happening to her. Ruiz had come back from his first visit to Carastrano already changing, sloughing off the cold repression of years, and, in doing so, he had become somebody entirely different. A man who would instantly attract women, with a magnetism that few men possessed. It was small wonder that what she had felt for Bruce had died such a quick and natural death.

His voice softened as he misunderstood her startled surprise and thought it was caused by what he had said.

"I am sorry I startled you so much. The idea had never occurred to you, it seems."

Hadn't it? Just what had been behind her preoccupation with the terms of old Don Diego's will? A genuine desire that an old name should not die out, that Ruiz should not, in effect, cheat to regain the home he loved and perhaps blame himself for it later—or a deeply hidden personal desire that this marriage should be more than just the business-like bargain it had started as? That she should really be his wife in all that the name implied.

As she remained silent, his hands slipped from her shoulders, his arms closed around her and drew her nearer to him.

"Would it be so very hard?"

Leigh tried to speak, but there seemed to be something

tight and constricted in her throat and she could only look up at him silently with widened eyes and lips that trembled slightly.

"We need not stay here all the time if you wished for more gaiety," he added with a note of persuasion in his deep, soft voice. "There could be visits to Mexico City and there is also a villa on the coast. I know money does not count for very much with you, but I am a rich man and you could have . . ."

"Please don't talk about the money side of it," she interrupted, managing to find her voice at last.

He smiled. "I thought you would say that." He was silent for a moment after that, then shook his dark head. "I find I have no glib words with which to persuade you," he said slowly. "I ask you to stay here with me instead of going back to England . . . and all I can speak of is money."

"It's only the insincere who can speak glibly when they want something."

That slipped out, but it seemed to please him. He held her closer, his dark head bent and she felt the warmth of his hands through her thin silk blouse.

"I don't think that I am physically repulsive to you." There was a little pause. "Am I?"

"No."

"You have lost the man you love." He felt her stiffen against him and misunderstood the reason. "But life could be rich here in Carastrano . . . and time deadens all pain. I know that myself."

Leigh turned so that she could look up at him. "Did you love her very much?"

He smiled and the dark head moved in negation. "I thought I did, but all that died long ago. One thinks at the time that the pain will last for ever, but . . ." He shrugged. "Then one day it is gone and one realises that love is just a romantic myth."

"And now you don't believe in love at all?" she asked quietly.

"The idealistic love that romanticists believe in?" He shook his head again. "If a man and woman find they can live together in companionship, isn't that enough?"

"I suppose so," Leigh agreed, but she wanted to tell him

that his reasoning was all wrong. Love was real and came only once. It was the infatuations that died, as hers for Bruce had died so easily and quickly when faced with real love.

Some slight touch of worry must have shown in her face, because he turned her so that he could watch her expression more closely, then his arms tightened and, bending his head, he kissed her as he had that night in Korveston. Again there was the quick leap of fire between them, a swift tide that carried both away from the shores of reality, far out on the sea of enchantment, while impetuous passion bound them together in an age-old bond.

After a moment he held her away from him and looked down into her flushed face. For a moment she met the rather quizzical smile in his eyes, then her glance dropped.

"Was that . . . to persuade me?"

For a moment he appeared to ponder that, then shook his head. "No, *querida*. I think it was to prove to you that even the pain of losing the man you love can be forgotten."

She rested in the curve of his arm, wishing she could tell him that Bruce meant nothing to her now, but how could she confess her love for him when he had said nothing of loving her, even though passion could swiftly rise between them? She was grateful though that he found her desirable enough to feel the urge to make love to her. She could not feel any pain yet that he did not love her—even though that might come later—because he so obviously felt desire for her. It would have been quite unbearable if he had asked her to stay at Carastrano and give him a son if he felt nothing at all for her.

Her attempt to make him realise his duty towards Carastrano had recoiled in a way she had not expected, but she could not be sorry that it had happened like this.

"Is it . . . only for Carastrano?" she heard herself ask a little diffidently, and could not help feeling that it was rather a silly question when she had been pointing out all along that it was for Carastrano and nothing and nobody else.

He looked at her for a moment, then shook his head, as if he had just realised something.

"Not entirely," he said slowly, as if he was still surprised to find that something else besides Carastrano could be part of it. "Perhaps it is also because I find that you have become part of my life. Even if we cannot love, I think we could find happiness together," and he bent his head and kissed her again, fastening his fingers into the hair at the back of her head this time and holding her mouth against his, even though she made no attempt to deny her response to him.

"Would it be so very hard?" he asked when he at last lifted his head, but when she tried to speak and could say nothing but whisper his name he shook his head and smiled gently. "Do not try to decide now. We shall return to Carastrano and you will think about it." He turned her towards their waiting horses. "And then perhaps tonight you will give me the answer I want to hear."

So they rode back to Carastrano and, as he had instructed, she thought about it, but she could have given him her answer then and there. To leave Carastrano and let someone else take her place would have been like tearing every living and vital thing from her body.

When he came to her that night the windows were open to the soft breeze that came down from the nearby hills and brought with it the scent of the roses of Carastrano. If she had had to go away she knew she would always have remembered that more than anything else—except the man she left there at Carastrano—but now the scent of the roses would be with her for always.

She was sitting in front of the mirror, brushing out her long burnished hair, when he came into the room. She paused involuntarily, the brush suspended in mid-air, and he took it from her hand, sitting down at her side on the long dressing stool.

"Let me do that for you."

Leigh sat perfectly still as a firm brown hand drew the brush through the silken mass. Suddenly he dropped the brush and lifted the softness of her hair up to his face, bending his head to touch his darkly tanned cheek against it.

"You have beautiful hair, *querida*. Do not ever cut it."

"I have been tempted to sometimes," she said tremulously, hardly aware now of what she was saying. "It's an awful nuisance."

"Very beautiful and very feminine," he corrected. "I do not like these short heads."

Leigh smiled at that, but still rather tremulously. "They do say 'long on hair, short on brains.' "

"I could give them a testimony how wrong they are. I once had a very efficient secretary . . . but I prefer my very lovely wife," he added huskily.

Leigh felt herself tremble slightly. "When I used to work for you, I never thought it could be like this."

"I think we must both have been hiding from each other," he said softly. Then suddenly he laughed with rueful amusement. "They are wily, these old ones. I wonder if he knew this would happen."

"Perhaps he did." She glanced at him momentarily, then away again, shy at meeting the warm dark glance. "You . . . you don't mind?"

He shook his head, smiling again. "A man would be a fool to wish that he had come here alone, and lived the rest of his life alone. I am glad that I did not make the mistake of allowing you to go back to England." Then his hands gripped her shoulders, the dark eyes searched her face. "And you, Leigh Aldoret? Do you mind that it happens like this?"

"No, I don't mind at all, she said very softly, and that seemed to be answer enough, for his hands left her shoulders and he drew her closer into his arms, bending his head to bury his lips in the warm curve of her throat.

This was enough to begin with, and perhaps, if the fates were kind, love would come later.

CHAPTER 12

LEIGH was brushing her hair when a hand touched her shoulder. She smiled, without turning.

"If this is a guessing game, I only need one guess!" She did turn then, her smile becoming slightly impish. "There's only one man who manages to turn my bones to water."

Ruiz smiled. "I'm glad of that." He brushed her lips lightly with his own and for a moment seemed as if he was going to release her, then he drew her fully into his arms and bent his head to kiss her with an almost deliberate sensuality that set her heart pounding and almost literally, as she had jokingly said, turned her bones to water. At any rate, even if that most unlikely metamorphosis did not really happen, she was conscious of a delicious languor that had a lot to do with sending all the strength from her body.

He grinned almost mischievously when he at last lifted his head. "Did Bruce Jermyn ever kiss you like that?"

Leigh felt herself flushing, but she laughed too. "No, he didn't. You have a way all of your own."

Again that almost mischievous grin turned his lips. "And you like it better?"

"Much better," she replied in his own tone. Was he really the same man as the iceberg she had worked for in England? Sometimes she had the feeling that the gnomes had made a switch-over and left a changeling when she was not looking.

"I am flattered." Then suddenly he became serious. "You do not miss him so much now?"

"I don't miss him at all," Leigh said instantly.

"That is good. I said the pain and the loss would die." He took her chin between thin, strong fingers. "I doubt that I would let him have you back now."

Leigh smiled and shook her head. "He's engaged to Stella now and both of them are very happy."

"As happy as we are?"

"They couldn't possibly be."

He laughed softly, touching his lips to her bare shoulder as he sat down at her side, and took the hairbrush from her, just as he had done on that first evening when their marriage had changed from being only a business bargain into something wonderful and real.

It was about three weeks later that the letter from Stella arrived. When Leigh learned that her sister would be flying out to make a film in Mexico she received the news with mixed feelings.

Of course it would be nice to see her sister again. After all, blood is thicker than water, and she had been devoted to Stella for so long that it was difficult now to regard her as someone who had to be treated cautiously, and had feet of clay in addition to being distinctly treacherous. She was prepared to believe that Stella had experienced remorse for what she had done to her, Leigh. But that did not mean the hurt could be wiped out and forgotten entirely, as if it was a smear on a dirty window.

To anyone in Leigh's present position, with a husband she now knew she adored, the thought of the radiant Stella arriving to exert an age-old feminine influence on a man who was far more relaxed and, therefore, impressionable—possibly?—than he had been a few months ago was a little alarming. At the same time there was a quick throb of eagerness because Stella was 'family,' and she wanted all the members of her family to know how happy she was.

"It will be nice to see Stella again," she said, a little slowly, to her husband. She added: "She says she will be playing opposite Ramon Talmonte. Isn't that the man we met in the restaurant when we first arrived out here?"

Ruiz nodded, his eyes flickering curiously over his wife.

"Yes. Apparently he is very popular." He paused for a moment and then suggested: "There is no reason why the house in Mexico City shouldn't be opened up. I will make arrangements for some staff to move in and air the place, and then your sister can stay with us there." When they had first arrived there had been a tenant leasing the house, but subsequently it had become vacant.

Leigh tried to look as if she was pleased by the idea.

"And you won't mind?" she asked. "I mean, it won't be a nuisance for you?"

"Of course not."

"There's no reason why she shouldn't stay at a hotel," with the faint hope that he might agree. "After all, she won't be alone. There'll be other members of the company with her."

Ruiz's dark eyes developed a mild look of teasing, and at the same time she suspected they were challenging her.

"Don't tell me you haven't got a lot to talk to your sister about when she arrives," he said. "Your mother will be anxious for all the details when Stella returns, and if you fail to supply her with them how will the glad news get around that your marriage is a success and you are happy out here?"

Leigh blushed delightfully, and fell to her knees beside his chair. She felt his fingers play in her hair as he drew her towards him and lightly kissed her brow.

"You are happy, aren't you, *querida*?" he breathed softly. "So happy?"

"So happy," she answered, and the breath caught in her throat because she was in actual fact quite ecstatically happy.

A few days later they flew to Mexico City and installed themselves in the Aldoret town house, a building remarkably like Carastrano, even to the inner courtyard and the singing fountain. There was a feeling of great continuity in this town house, as if generations of Aldorets had lived there and left their mark on the place, and been anxious that their successors should be impressed by what they did. It was more formal than Carastrano, breathing of formal receptions and long-drawn-out dinners, and echoing to the swish of silken skirts and lacy mantillas. In the dining-room, where a portrait of Don Diego hung above the fireplace, the furnishings were so sombre and yet so sumptuous that they quite took Leigh's breath away.

She went round fingering the quality of the damask that hung before the windows, and the patina on the furniture was so remarkable that she was quite sure the domestics of the household possessed some secret—or had, until they were dispersed by incoming tenants—which they had imparted to the furniture, accounting for the satin sheen that lay over chairs and tables and great side-tables alike.

There was a large quantity of silver in the dining-room

that had become tarnished in recent months, and Ruiz suggested that they might get rid of some of it. He also suggested that it might amuse her some time or other to give the entire house a face-lift and re-furnish it . . . a suggestion which shocked her until she realised he was not entirely serious. But he seemed to think it natural that a young wife should want to make alterations. In Leigh's case, however, when she thought of her comfortable but distinctly homely background the very idea seemed both ludicrous and impertinent.

She assured him that she was more than content with conditions as they were.

She selected a room for Stella on the first floor of the house, and she was very certain her sister would appreciate it because it was not unlike a stage set. The bed coverlet was richly embroidered and the furniture was all constructed from dark Spanish oak. There was plenty of wardrobe space and a quantity of mirrors, and the bathroom that adjoined it was sumptuously equipped. If Leigh knew anything at all about Stella she would sink into such a background as if it was her rightful setting, and any thought of moving into a hotel and relieving her sister and brother-in-law of the need to entertain her would never enter into her head.

Not that Leigh wished Stella to feel unwanted when she arrived in Mexico City. She wanted to be hospitable and to make Stella feel at home, but at the same time she wished she could be absolutely sure that Stella would repay her hospitality with a method of behaviour that would cause her few uneasy moments. She knew that she would never forget what had happened in the case of Bruce. And Ruiz was too important—her present state of happiness was too precious—to be put in danger.

Nevertheless, she was careful to conceal from Ruiz that she had any doubts about her sister. She thought sometimes that he looked at her quizzically when she stressed how much she was looking forward to Stella's arrival, and she wondered whether he sensed how secretly uneasy she was. But if he did he said nothing. She sometimes wished he would, and then she might have dared to confess her fears in advance.

They drove to the airport to meet Stella on a brilliant day

when Korveston and her old life seemed very very far away ... which in actual fact it was, of course. During the drive to the airport Leigh strove to bolster definitely flagging spirits by chattering as if she was wildly excited, and it was only when she glanced at Ruiz's dark, attractive face that a sudden agony of apprehension seized her, and she wondered why she didn't think up some pretext there and then for preventing Stella staying with them and going straight to a hotel instead. But it was impossible to think of anything that would have convinced both Stella and Ruiz himself that the actress would be better off with the other members of the film company in one of Mexico City's well-run hotels.

She had to go through with it. It was written that Stella should stay with them, and she could only hope—hope—*hope* that everything would be all right!

Stella hurled herself into her arms when they met on the tarmac. She was dressed as usual with infinite care, and she looked so startlingly attractive that Leigh's heart sank.

"You're looking quite marvellous, darling," Stella gushed, once the somewhat frenzied greeting was over and the two girls had separated. There was the old bright sparkle of mockery in her eyes, despite the fact that they also beamed with affection. "Quite the married woman! So smart and dignified I hardly knew you at first!"

Ruiz smiled.

"You think she is looking well?" he asked.

"Oh, very well! Never better, in fact! You must be a highly satisfactory husband."

Her beautiful eyes ogled him.

"May I kiss you, Ruiz?" she asked. "After all, we are related now, aren't we?" And without waiting for his consent she reached up and laid her petal-soft lips to his dark cheek, enveloping him in a wave of her perfume that was very much stronger, and definitely more exciting, than anything Leigh allowed herself to use.

"Um," she said, when she stepped back and fluttered her long eyelashes at him, "I think I'm going to like having you for a brother-in-law!"

Ruiz did not make a similar observation about having her for a sister-in-law, but after her luggage had been stowed away in the boot of his car he seemed to think it quite natural that she should occupy the seat beside him at the wheel, and that his wife should be ensconced in the back of the car. He seemed to be under the impression that that was what Leigh would prefer in any case, and as they drove away from the airport with the Mexican sunshine spilling all about them Leigh's fingernails dug deep into the palms of her hands, and she had actually to take herself to task because she knew she was reacting quite ridiculously to her sister's arrival.

She was actually allowing herself to believe that Stella would do something to wreck her marriage, and if she went on thinking along those lines the next few weeks would be sheer torment for her. And, in any case, Ruiz wasn't Bruce. He was a very, very different type of man, and this reflection finally persuaded her to behave more normally, and to look upon Stella much as she had done in the old days, before she had had any reason to doubt her sister.

Only one revelation shook her slightly when they reached the house, and Stella was unpacking her things in her room.

"Have you and Bruce announced your engagement yet?" Leigh asked, and Stella turned from the wardrobe and admitted that there wasn't going to be any engagement. A shadow crossed her perfect face as if she was striving to prevent her unhappiness from showing in it, and there was a catch in her voice as she made the admission.

"It's just one of those things," she said, as she shook out a gossamer evening dress. "Apparently Bruce was never really in love with me. It was the glamorous, film-star me that attracted him! He told me so!"

"Oh, darling, I am sorry!" The words were wrenched from Leigh impulsively, and in that moment she was genuinely sorry. "I—I just don't know what to say."

Stella shrugged.

"It's all right, darling. There isn't much you can say in the circumstances, except perhaps that I—deserve what has happened!" a misty gleam in her eyes and a wryness at the corners of her lovely mouth. And whether it was by accident or design or simply as the result of pent-up emotion that lovely mouth actually quivered suddenly, and she had to turn away to hide her distress. "If you don't mind," she begged, in a choked voice, "I'd rather not discuss it now."

"Of course," Leigh said immediately, sympathetically... although, after all, it was only poetic justice that had overtaken Stella. "I understand perfectly." She added hurriedly: "We'll have to make things so gay for you while you're here that you won't think of Bruce, and will stop making yourself unhappy by brooding. It won't do you any good at all to brood, and Mexico City really is a wonderful place, and I'm sure you'll love it here. Ruiz has lots of friends and we'll introduce you. You won't have time to be unhappy!"

"Thank you, darling." Stella turned to her gratefully, but her long lashes were hiding her eyes by this time and it was impossible to tell what she was really thinking and feeling. She brightened determinedly. "Well, hadn't we better go down and join your husband? I think you're very lucky to have married him. He strikes me as quite exciting... unusually exciting!" She added a touch of lipstick to her lips and mascara to her eyes. "And this is a really marvellous house!"

"Wait until you see Carastrano," Leigh replied.

Her sister smiled at her.

"Darling, I'm determined to see Carastrano," she assured her softly. "I shall probably stay with you for ages and ages, and you'll have a frightful job getting rid of me in the end."

Leigh crossed her fingers, unseen by the other girl.

"Oh, *no*!" she said to herself, with a feeling of alarm.

Ruiz was awaiting them in the main sitting-room of the house, and once more he put himself out to be attentive to the guest. He provided her with a drink before they went in to dinner, saw that she was comfortably disposed of in one of the most relaxing chairs, admired her gown with the knowledgeable air of a man who knew a lot about such matters, and placed her at his right hand in the splendidly furnished dining-room.

He was formal in the way he addressed her, but that she very quickly put right.

"You mustn't call me Miss Nordett," she told him. "That is my professional name, and certainly not for use by the members of my own family. The name is Stella, in case you don't know," she ended with a gay laugh.

"Stella?" He acknowledged her graciousness in permitting him to use it with a little bow, and repeated the name several times as if he liked the sound of it. "Stella? That means star, I think?" His own dark eyes rested on her, and he seemed quite fascinated by the depth and brilliance of hers. "Dark star," he said very softly, and somehow thoughtfully, as he lit a cigarette.

Surprisingly Stella looked faintly disturbed, and she even shuddered slightly.

"That sounds ominous," she remarked. "In fact I don't think I want to be a dark star. I'd much rather be one that goes on soaring and soaring and growing brighter and brighter. A star only dims when the dawn is near, and I much prefer high noon."

"Don't worry," Leigh assured her kindly, "your high noon is likely to last for a long time, Stella. You are at your very zenith now so far as your career is concerned."

"Am I?" But Stella's look was doubtful. Once again her glance entangled with Ruiz's, and she made a statement that could have come straight from her heart. "I think I would rather have a successful marriage than continue to be a successful actress. I'm growing a little tired of acting, and the demands it makes on me, but marriage—if the looks of you two are anything to go by!—is a highly satisfying and a rewarding thing."

Once again Ruiz bowed to her.

"You are so right, Stella," he assured her, and then he smiled directly at Leigh.

She felt her heart flutter in gratitude, and she spoke quickly to Stella; anxious all at once to give her some comfort and consolation, because she had lost Bruce.

"I said that we want you to have a good time while you're here, and I might as well tell you now that we've arranged a small dinner-party to welcome you here, and I don't think your dinner partner will be in two minds as to whether you're a star or not. In fact, I know he won't!"

"Oh?" Stella said, looking interested. "This sounds very intriguing."

"It's someone you'll be meeting sooner or later, but we thought it might as well be sooner."

"Tell me," Stella begged, looking almost childishly attractive. "I can't wait!"

"Ramon Talmonte." Leigh smiled at her. "Your leading

man—and the biggest wolf in Mexico City! We thought you might like to meet him before the official introduction."

Stella agreed that she would, even though she was not particularly fond of wolves.

"But perhaps he's not as bad as he's painted," she added, "and in any case it will be fun putting salt on a wolf's tail!"

They went on talking about general topics after that, and Leigh admired her sister's acting. If she loved Bruce she must be feeling dreadfully unhappy, but she was making an extremely good effort to hide it. Upstairs she had indicated that she was very much upset—too upset even to discuss the break with Bruce—but from the way her eyes sparkled occasionally when she exchanged badinage with Ruiz the distraught condition of mind was difficult to believe in.

Two nights later the guests arrived for the dinner-party that was to welcome her to Mexico City. Leigh dressed with care for the occasion, choosing from her by now extensive wardrobe a very lovely gown which she and Ruiz had bought together soon after their arrival in Mexico City. It was of deep sapphire velvet, and it was cunningly embroidered with seed pearls and had a slim ankle-length skirt. It was so strikingly elegant that no other ornamentation was really needed, but just as she was standing regarding herself in her mirror and wondering about a necklace of sapphires and diamonds which Ruiz had given her, and a matching bracelet to go with it, he came in through the door from his dressing-room and laid a flat leather case down on the dressing-table. First he kissed her, long and lingeringly, in a way that set the blood pounding through her veins, then he told her she looked beautiful and lifted the lid of the case. A shining row of pearls glistened up at them.

Leigh gasped.

"Oh, but they're wonderful!"

"They will look even more wonderful round your neck."

Slim, vital fingers fastened them about her neck, and then he handed her pendant ear-rings of pear-shaped pearls to fasten on herself. For a moment she stared into the mirror as if she could hardly believe that it was her own reflection that faced her, then she turned impulsively and drew his dark head down to kiss him.

"I don't know how to thank you for all that you've given me," she told him.

"You have given me far more," he answered her quietly. "I had forgotten what it was like to be alive. When one withdraws and lives in a shell, that is mere existence." For one moment more he held her, then he put her from him gently, smiling quizzically. "Go and see if your sister is ready," he advised. "Remember, this is an important evening for her, and we must pay her as much attention as possible."

Just before she reached the door of her bedroom he called her back. She saw that his dark face was turned to her, and he was regarding her very intently.

"*Querida*, this meeting with your sister does not cause you too much pain?" he asked.

"Because of Bruce, you mean?" She smiled and shook her head. "It doesn't cause me any pain at all. I got over that long ago."

"That is good," he said. "And it pleases you that your sister is here?"

She hesitated for just a moment, then assured him with a measure of truth:

"Yes, it's lovely to see her again."

Ruiz seemed satisfied.

"One day we must invite your friend Kerry to stay with us," he suggested. An almost boyish grin crossed his face. "And find someone like Ramon Talmonte to marry her off to!" he added.

Leigh dimpled delightfully.

"Poor Ramon! Tonight he's to be shattered by Stella, so for the moment I think we'll spare him Kerry. But I agree it would be wonderful if she would come and stay with us. And when she does... well, we'll find someone for her to marry."

"But first you have to marry off Stella," he remarked a little drily.

Leigh went along to her sister's room, where she found Stella in need of someone to zip up the back of her gorgeous glittering gown. She was quick to admire Leigh's magnificent velvet, and her eyes fastened on the new pearl necklace as if each pearl was a magnet that drew them. She touched the necklace lightly and appreciatively.

"I don't need to ask you if they're real," she said.

"Ruiz has just given them to me," Leigh admitted.

"Lucky girl!" Stella turned away and studied her own reflection in the mirror and a quite extraordinary expression crossed her face. She lowered her eyes and studied the delicate tips of her own slender fingers. "I've already congratulated you, darling," she said drawlingly, "on a highly successful marriage. But by 'successful' I mean that it's turned out surprisingly well. You and Ruiz made a sort of bargain, didn't you, and it worked?"

"A—a bargain?" Leigh stammered.

Stella's long eyelashes fluttered upwards and she turned and touched her sister's cheek caressingly.

"Yes. I guessed, of course ... although you did put on an act for Mother's benefit. But now that you're actually married to him you'll have to be very clever if you're going to keep Ruiz. He has an eye for beauty, particularly cool English beauty! I felt embarrassed by the way he sat and stared at me tonight!"

Leigh could hardly believe the evidence of her ears.

"That was because you're my sister," she said. "And—and naturally he admires you. Everyone does!"

Stella's eyes grew bright with a kind of mockery, and then she answered soothingly:

"Oh, very well, darling, have it your own way. But take my advice and keep him well away from all the Latin lovelies out here!"

They went downstairs to meet the first of the guests, and Leigh felt as if a large part of her pleasure in the evening had evaporated. She introduced Stella mechanically to Ramon Talmonte and the rest of the guests, and when she saw Ruiz looking at her sharply she strove hard to make it appear that everything was entirely normal.

But it was not. Stella, she suspected, had been rendered jealous by the sight of her expensive pearl necklace, and no doubt it had made her catty ... but there was always the possibility that it was not just cattiness, and that she had been issuing a warning. If she had met Ruiz Aldoret, and got nicely acquainted with him before she met Bruce, it would have been Ruiz she would have earmarked for herself, not Bruce!

And now she was regretting that she had not met Ruiz first.

Leigh found it difficult to believe that her sister was such a menace to her own future happiness, but past experience had taught her to be wary. She knew she could never trust Stella, and although she did trust Ruiz the situation was one that made her far from happy. If only Ruiz hadn't suggested that she should stay with them it would have been easier, and as it was Leigh hoped that when her sister started film-making it would be different.

She seemed quite attracted by Ramon Talmonte, and for a few weeks life developed a more even note again. Stella wanted to see everything there was to see in Mexico City, and taste all the delights of the city, and fortunately Ramon seemed eager to show them to her. She went about with him a good deal, and the studio claimed her for another large part of her time. Leigh felt as if she was living on the side of a volcano, and she was only really happy when her sister was out of the house, but she also felt horribly guilty because her suspicions of Stella included Ruiz.

And Ruiz was such a wonderful husband that it was all horribly unfair. But most unfortunately Stella and unfairness seemed to go together.

Life was limping along in this somewhat difficult fashion when Maria, the housekeeper, who spoke excellent English, tapped on the door of the main salon one day and told Leigh, when she called out to her to come in, that an English *señor* wished to see her.

"An English *señor*? What is his name?" Leigh demanded.

"Señor Bruce."

"*Bruce . . .*?"

Leigh waited for no more, but walked swiftly through to the hall where Bruce was standing and looking slightly awkward, as if his surroundings overpowered him and in any case he was not really certain about his welcome. But when Leigh—the new, gracious, beautifully dressed Leigh who was also mistress of this most imposing house in unfamiliar Mexico City—hove in sight, he forgot his awkwardness, forgot his uncertainty and made the mistake of assuming a very great deal. He looked at her with a bright light in his eyes and tried without hesitation to take her in his arms.

Shocked and startled, Leigh moved quickly out of his reach.

"What are you doing here, Bruce?" she demanded coolly.

Surprise, hurt, and then indignation registered in his expression. Forced to desist from trying to seize hold of her, he muttered sulkily:

"You don't seem very pleased to see me."

"In the circumstances, that should be understandable," Leigh replied with commendable calm. What in heaven's name had brought him to Mexico City? "Did you come to see Stella?" she asked.

"So she's already arrived," he commented.

"Yes, she's been here nearly a fortnight." She paused for a moment, but he did not say anything, so she repeated, "Did you come to see her?" But even as she put this unlikely question to him she realised that it was highly unlikely that he would have behaved as he had just done if his sole purpose was to see Stella.

"Your charming sister?" He laughed shortly. "It's all over between Stella and myself. I've been a damn fool, but at least I woke up in time."

"*You've* been a fool?" Leigh echoed. "Doesn't it occur to you that in addition you've also been something else? You let me down, and you let Stella down—"

"Is that what she told you?" he interrupted.

"Didn't you let her down?"

"I'm sure she's told you a beautiful sob story," he said sarcastically. "I'd like to hear what that pure white sister of yours said about me, but given time I'll tell you a lot about her."

"I won't have you refer to a close relative of mine like that!" Leigh blazed at him, because Stella was, after all, a very close relative, and this man had behaved badly in any case. And now he was trying to justify himself.

"All right, I won't if you say so. But you'd better brief me on what she did say to you. I'd like to know how I stand."

Leigh frowned. This was a most unpleasant situation, and she disliked it extremely.

"There would be no purpose in Stella lying to me," she replied primly. "What she told me must have been the truth

. . . that you were fascinated by the glamorous side of a film star, and then you recovered from your infatuation."

He shook his head at her. He walked up to her and gripped her by her arms, tightening his hold as she tried to free herself. A note of desperation entered his voice.

"When are you going to face the truth about your sister?" he demanded. "When are you going to face it that she's like no other member of your family? She's the most self-centred young woman I've ever met, and she doesn't care a jot for you . . . for anyone apart from herself! She'd break up anyone's life and not care at all. I know her, I know the truth about her, Leigh! She was just amusing herself with me. She was bored, and it was part of a game. She never meant to marry me. If you hadn't come in when you did and caught us in what looked like a compromising situation—"

Leigh laughed at him.

"Oh, Bruce, spare me," she begged. "It was a compromising situation, and you know it. And although you may deny it now you fell madly in love with her—"

"I can assure you I'm not in love with her any longer."

Leigh shrugged, amazed at herself for her hardness because she actually felt little or no pity for him—and even less for Stella. But she had to make him believe she was championing Stella.

"Then all I can say is that you're very good at falling in and out of love," with contempt in her eyes. "And I disapprove very strongly of your coming here and accusing my sister of breaking faith with you."

He laughed shortly. "She never does take the blame for anything, does she . . . always the snow-white little innocent. One of these days you're going to find out what she's really like—and I hope the shock doesn't come too hard!"

Leigh succeeded in freeing herself and quickly moved back, away from him.

"If you continue to speak like that, I'll have to tell you to go. In any case, why *have* you come here? It's rather an awkward situation, you know."

"I've come to take you home," was the startling announcement.

There was silence for a moment, while Leigh struggled to make sense out of what she was hearing.

"Have you forgotten that I'm married to Ruiz?" she said at last.

"It's only a business marriage. You said so yourself." He moved towards her, as if he would have caught hold of her again, but Leigh quickly evaded him. "Leigh, you've got to come back with me. We belong together. Stella was just a passing madness."

"And now you want to carry on where our engagement ended?"

Her voice was so quiet that he misread her meaning and nodded eagerly.

"You can get an annulment."

"But suppose I don't want to?" Leigh asked quietly.

"You said . . . I mean . . ." His voice died away into silence.

"I think we'd better get one thing clear," Leigh said evenly. "I don't want to go back as things were, Bruce. Even if it hadn't been like this, with you letting Stella down, I still wouldn't want to leave Ruiz. I happen to love him now. Our marriage might have started off as just a business arrangement, but it's real now, so you see there's no question of an annulment."

His eyes narrowed and a flush of anger came into his face. "So Stella was right! She said you couldn't trust a dago to keep a bargain like that."

"Don't ever use that word again!" Leigh snapped icily.

He had the grace to look somewhat ashamed. "Sorry," he muttered.

"And what has Stella got to do with it?" Leigh demanded. "Did you tell her it was only a business proposition?" Was she misjudging him just slightly? Perhaps Stella had found out it was only a business marriage and had refused to marry Bruce because of that, believing her sister was still in love with him and leaving him free for when the business marriage ended. But in that case, why put the blame on Bruce and say that he did not love her and had only been bemused by glamour?

No, that theory could not be right. Stella could not know anything about her sister's marriage having started as only a business proposition or she would have mentioned it when she first arrived.

"I didn't mean to tell her," Bruce excused himself. "It just . . . slipped out."

"Did it?" Leigh said sceptically. Quite obviously he was lying.

Suddenly Stella appeared in the long french windows that stood open to the garden.

"Leigh, darling, did you know . . ." She broke off suddenly, one hand going up to her mouth with a gasp as she caught sight of Bruce. Her consternation was part genuine and part assumed. "Oh—you here!"

Leigh immediately went over to her and slipped an arm comfortingly around her shoulders.

"He's just leaving, darling."

"No, I'm not," Bruce said belligerently. "We've got one or two things to clear up before I go." He glared over at Stella. "Just what sort of lying story have you been telling Leigh?"

Stella gave her sister an almost pitiful look. "Leigh, I don't understand. What's he talking about?"

"You wouldn't know, I suppose," he snapped sarcastically. "You didn't deliberately break up our engagement just for the fun of it, never intending to marry me? You didn't laugh at me and . . . and start taunting me about Ruiz Aldoret when I told you Leigh had entered into a business marriage so you shouldn't blame yourself about breaking the engagement?"

Stella turned to Leigh with pitiful entreaty in her eyes. "Leigh, what in heaven's name is he talking about?"

"Oh, pack it up!" Bruce almost shouted. "You know damn well what I'm talking about. You came over here determined to break up Leigh's marriage, because you decided at the wedding that you'd rather like to have Ruiz Aldoret's money for yourself."

Leigh abruptly withdrew her arm from about Stella and went over to the bell pull, but he forestalled her.

"Oh no, you don't. You're going to listen to what I have to say."

"I think you've said quite enough," and she succeeded in reaching the bell pull, which she tugged with vigorous determination. "Mr. Jermyn is leaving now, Chita," she said in Spanish. "Will you show him out?"

Bruce quietened his voice now that the housekeeper was there, speaking in English, which she could not understand.

"All right, I'll go—but maybe you'll have cause to want to see me again. I'm staying nearby, at the Mendito. If you want me . . ."

"I don't think I shall need to trouble you," Leigh replied evenly.

"No?" He gave a short, grim little laugh, glancing briefly at Stella and then back to Leigh. "Maybe you might decide to go back to England with me after all," and with that he turned and accompanied Chita out of the room.

A little silence fell as the door closed behind them. "You . . . you didn't believe him, did you?" Stella asked hesitantly at last.

"Of course not," Leigh told her with quick reassurance.

"I . . . I'm glad you didn't." Then she gave her sister a puzzled, slightly worried look. "Leigh, what did he mean about a business marriage?"

"Then you really don't know anything about it?"

"Of course not," Stella denied instantly. "You didn't believe I . . ."

"No, I didn't think you knew," Leigh said, her tone again becoming reassuring.

"But what did he mean? I thought . . . I mean, you seemed to be so happy . . ."

"I am happy," Leigh said quietly.

"Was the marriage a business arrangement, though?"

"Yes. Ruiz had to be married to inherit Carastrano, and I thought it would make things easier for you and Bruce."

Stella had the grace to look ashamed.

"But, darling, you shouldn't have done anything like that," she protested, apparently aghast.

Leigh smiled. "As it happened, everything has turned out for the best," she said. "In the beginning I wasn't in the least bit in love with Ruiz, and if there had been any question of the bargain including providing an heir for Carastrano I wouldn't have agreed for one moment . . . then."

"Then it was to be a temporary affair. A divorce as quickly and decently as it could be arranged?"

This time it was Leigh who looked horrified by the bald sound of such very unpleasant words.

"But not any longer," she tried to convince her sister. "When we seemed to get on very well together Ruiz suggested making our marriage a real one... and it is very real now!"

Stella made a quick gesture which indicated that she found the whole thing difficult to comprehend.

"Oh, heavens, Leigh," she exclaimed, "what a mess! What an awful and unnecessary mess! If you hadn't married... or at least, if it was still possible for an annulment...?" glancing sideways at her sister. "I suppose it would be possible to get a divorce if you're not absolutely certain about the future? And I don't see how you can be one hundred per cent sure at this stage!"

Leigh smiled at her confidently.

"I am sure. I don't want a divorce. I told you before, everything turned out for the best. I've been in love with Ruiz for ages now. I don't want Bruce back."

Stella bit her lip.

"You *are* absolutely certain about that? After all, you were very fond of him once!"

"I am absolutely sure, and fondness isn't love. I—I know that now."

Stella's glance at her was just a little quizzical. There was, at the same time, a look in her eyes whioh Leigh quite failed to understand.

"Oh, well..." Stella shrugged her shapely shoulders and apparently dismissed the whole thing. "It just shows you how many mistakes you can make in life!"

Leigh smiled at her with a return of her old fondness.

"Now let's forget Bruce and go and get changed, shall we?" she said. "Ruiz is coming back to pick us up when he finishes his business conference and take us on some more sight-seeing."

During the drive that afternoon Stella appeared to be somewhat preoccupied, but she expressed herself as highly appreciative when it was over and graciously thanked Ruiz. That evening, just before dinner, she left her room before Leigh, and made her way down to the salon where they always had a drink before the dinner-gong sounded. Ruiz was standing by the cocktail cabinet, and he turned and smiled at her enquiringly as he lifted his glass.

Stella demurely accepted a drink from her brother-in-law.

Leigh realised she was a little late, and she hurried down to join the others. She had already discovered that Stella had left her room ahead of her and she expected to find her in the salon. Since her talk with her sister that afternoon her suspicions of her had been somewhat lulled, therefore it was all the more a shock when she pushed the door open slightly and heard this conversation going on:

"I'm glad I found you alone, Ruiz," Stella was saying, in her beautiful soft, clear voice. "There's something I've been trying to say to you ever since I arrived . . . but it wasn't exactly easy, and I put it off. However, something happened this afternoon that made me realise I've got to blunder in where angels fear to tread, if you'll try to see my point of view."

Leigh heard Ruiz's quiet but somewhat surprised answer.

"If there is anything I can do to help you please let me know what it is."

"It's about my sister . . . and Bruce!"

"Oh, yes?" from Ruiz, in the same polite tone.

"It's very difficult to talk about," Stella began somewhat more huskily, and Leigh never understood afterwards why she didn't instinctively move away. It was not her habit to listen-in on other people's conversations. But her own name had been mentioned, and she remained quite motionless just outside the door. "In fact, I don't quite know how to put it. But perhaps if I tell you that I know why Leigh married you—in order that you could inherit Carastrano—you will get the drift!"

There was a moment of silence, and then Ruiz said unemotionally:

"Yes?"

"So don't you think it's . . . rather unfair to keep her still tied to you? I mean—" and Leigh could almost see her flinging out her expressive hands—"it doesn't strike me that you're keeping your part of the bargain. She did so much for me that I feel I've got to get this matter put right."

"Then she has told you the real reason for our marriage?" he asked curtly.

"Well—not exactly. I happened to overhear her talking to someone about it."

"And who would she talk to about such a very personal matter?"

"Bruce."

"Ah!" Leigh heard him say, and but for the fact that she felt rooted to the spot she would have rushed in at this point. "The man she was once engaged to marry?"

"Yes." Stella's voice contained a tiny thrill of satisfaction. "Of course it's nothing to do with me, but I'm terribly fond of Leigh, and I know how devoted she was to Bruce at one time—"

"Please go on," Ruiz instructed her quietly.

Stella apparently drew a long breath, and then she put aside her diffidence and plunged into the story as she had decided she knew it.

"I was in the garden when he arrived. As a matter of fact, I was on my way back to the house when I saw his taxi come sweeping up to the front of the house. I didn't want to interrupt anything, so I waited out of sight at the far end of the hall while they greeted one another..." She drew another long breath. "If I could spare you I would, but—it was a very emotional meeting!"

Ruiz remained absolutely silent, and she went on:

"It was then that I overheard the bit about Leigh marrying you because you had to marry someone in order to get Carastrano. Leigh insisted that it was just a temporary affair, and—and—he wanted her to go back to England with him, but she said it was impossible. She was terribly distressed, and of course she's loyal. But I could tell that the meeting with Bruce was just too much for her."

"I had no idea he was in Mexico City," Ruiz said in an utterly colourless voice.

"You mean she—she didn't tell you?"

"No."

"Oh, dear!" Stella exclaimed. "That does make it all seem rather worse, doesn't it?"

"I'm not quite sure what you mean by worse," Ruiz remarked.

"Well, guilty! It makes them both sound very guilty."

"Does it?"

Oh, why was his speech so clipped and uninformative? Leigh wondered outside the door. It was utterly emotionless, and he didn't even sound particularly upset. And she asked herself too late why hadn't she told him about Bruce.

She waited a moment or so longer before entering the room, and during that time she heard Stella say:

"It's because I want her to be happy that I've said all this to you! Leigh is so deserving of happiness, and she means a lot to me. You do understand, don't you?"

"And you do not think I am making her happy?"

"She tries to pretend that she's happy, but she can't deceive me. I've known her since childhood, you see. We grew up together. It's because of me that this horrible mix-up occurred, and I want to put it right. That's why I determined to speak to you."

"Your devotion to your sister's interests does you credit," he remarked drily.

Stella made a soft sound, as if she appreciated his discernment. And then Leigh recovered the use of her legs and control over her will power and walked into the room. She managed to smile and look so normal that they neither of them suspected she had overheard anything at all of the recent conversation, and it seemed to require little effort on Ruiz's part to behave normally. Leigh had seldom known him as attentive to her as he was at dinner that night.

And as for Stella, she was all smiles and sparkle from the moment her sister walked into the room.

But Leigh realised a crisis had been reached in her life, and it was entirely her own fault. She should have let Ruiz know that Bruce had arrived from England, and because she hadn't a situation had been created that it might be difficult to resolve. She entertained no doubt at all that Stella had deliberately created this situation—if only for the reason that she was jealous of her sister's happiness—and if Stella was not to win in the end then Leigh knew she had to behave very circumspectly in the immediate future, and for the moment she must not reveal what she had overheard.

She must think the whole thing out for herself before trying to retrieve the situation.

That night, for the first time since their marriage had become a real marriage, Ruiz slept in his dressing-room. He went out after dinner to see some friends, and when he returned it was very late. It was perhaps natural that he should not disturb her, but she knew very well there was nothing natural about it—and the next morning he told her that he had to return to Carastrano immediately.

"I'll get packed straight away," Leigh said, already turning for the doors of her wardrobe, but he spoke decisively.

"There is no need. I shall be away for only a few days."

She started to say something, then fell silent. This was not the moment to have it out with him, and she had to let him go.

She helped him to pack his cases, and he asked suddenly:

"Why didn't you tell me your ex-fiancé has been in touch with you?"

"I meant to," she answered, "but there was no real chance of bringing up the subject."

"Perhaps you didn't think it important?" he suggested.

"N-no, it wasn't important." She gazed at him in a kind of agony. The only important thing was that he should turn and kiss her, but he didn't do so. He merely said something hurriedly about not wishing to miss his flight, and they went downstairs together. She stood biting her lips in the open front doorway as his car raced off to the airport.

After that the loneliness closed in. She wanted to go back to Carastrano too, but she could only follow him in her thoughts, tracing the flight of the aircraft on a map, visualising it as it would look as it came in sight of the low hills that surrounded Carastrano and started to descend.

"Just a few minutes and I'll be home," she would be thinking if she was on it.

Carastrano had become that to her. Home. Even more of a home than the one she had grown up in, although she would always love that too. This was different, though, because Carastrano was part of the man she loved.

It almost frightened her now when she thought of how nearly she had married Bruce. Then, when the romance of thinking herself in love had passed, she might have realised that she was really in love with the man she had worked for. Or perhaps that realisation would never have come and they would merely have settled down to a form of tepid companionship, both of them content because they knew of nothing different. And this was so very different.

If Stella had not come home on a visit . . . and now it was Stella who was having to pay in unhappiness for opening her sister's eyes to the fact that it was really Ruiz Aldoret she loved, not Bruce.

Leigh smiled softly. Where was Ruiz now? Had the plane landed yet? If she was with him she would feel his hand beneath her elbow as they mounted the steps to the terrace and every nerve in her body would be alive and singing because even his lightest touch could bring her happiness.

They would go into the cool hall and it would be more than just coming home. There would be memories of delirious happiness to wrap around her like a tangible, glowing veil . . . memories of Ruiz fresh from the shower, his skin bronzed and healthy, his black hair still damp and tousled . . . or sophisticated and perfectly dressed in evening clothes . . . gay and laughing in the Mexican riding clothes that suited him so well. Memories of standing in the portrait gallery, looking at the generations of Aldorets, moving along until she came to the blank portion of the wall that was reserved for future generations. Once there had been a danger that it would remain blank, but although there was as yet still no heir for Carastrano, she had always had the warm certainty in her heart that one day she would be able to tell the man she loved that he was not to be the last of the Aldorets. Sometimes he would find her standing there and he would slip an arm around her shoulders. Quite involuntarily her lips would curve into a smile and she would suspect that her eyes were betraying too much of what she felt about him, but she had long passed beyond caring about such things. He was a man any woman could be proud to love, even though there must be reticence to put it into actual words, because he had never said that he loved her.

A private little paradise of their own, she had thought—but what was happening now? Was he beginning to regret that he had ever allowed their marriage to change from the purely business affair it had once been? Or, in some way, was it . . . Bruce?

The next day Leigh decided to go to see Bruce in case, as well as Ruiz learning of him coming to the house, he might have contacted him and Bruce had said anything to cause further trouble; but when she called at the hotel where he was staying, it was only to be informed that he was out, and she returned to the house, but there was a restless moodiness in possession of her, so she went out again, walking aimlessly. She could not even talk to Stella, because her sister was spending the afternoon in her room with the green sun-blinds drawn and a splitting headache as a result of being out in the sun for too long, and in any case Leigh could no longer trust her.

Leigh felt miserably that she could no longer trust anyone. She walked about in the hot, blinding sunlight until she exhausted herself, and then she returned home.

CHAPTER 13

ODDLY enough, Leigh found herself remembering that other occasion when she had come home unexpectedly. . but this time it was rather different. Instead of withdrawing automatically, numbed with shock and pain, she merely slipped back out of sight and listened.

This was different. So very different. Just as before, she had come in by other than the front entrance, entering from long, open windows that led out to terraced gardens, but that was the only point of similarity. This time it was not so much pain she felt as cold disillusionment and the beginning of a firm resolve as she continued to listen to Stella speaking.

"I do think you might be a little more pleasant about it," the actress drawled with light mockery. "After all, it is to your advantage as well."

"Maybe I don't want to sink to quite the same level as you," Bruce retorted.

Stella shrugged. "Who worries what means are used so long as the end desired is achieved? Really, darling, you should thank me. I've already laid a little of the groundwork. I shouldn't be at all surprised if fairly soon you'll be able to persuade Leigh to go back to England with you."

"Oh no," Leigh said quietly, now appearing fully in the open windows. "You broke up my engagement, Stella, but I have no intention of allowing you to break up my marriage to Ruiz."

It was odd really how one could swing right over to the other extreme at almost a moment's notice. A few minutes ago she would have believed nothing bad about Stella, but now everything that had puzzled her, every last little detail fell suddenly into place and her disillusionment was absolute and complete, and she knew that Bruce had been speaking the truth when he said Stella had been playing with them when she broke up their engagement.

Stella turned slowly. For a moment her expression was quite blank, then slowly the mocking smile came over it.

"You really do have a penchant for appearing when you're least expected, don't you, darling?" she drawled, without the least sign of shame or of being perturbed in any way.

"In this instance, it's just as well that I did appear," Leigh said with the same quietness that had been in her voice when she first made her presence known.

"Forewarned is forearmed?" Stella jibed.

"Yes. You might have been able to succeed if I hadn't known it was you causing trouble." She paused and then asked slowly, "Just what did you tell Ruiz to make him go off to Carastrano so suddenly like that?"

"Wouldn't you like to know?" Stella said mockingly.

Leigh smiled slightly. "I suppose it was really too much to expect that you would tell me. But I can probably find out from Ruiz himself. There are certain advantages in being actually married to a man if one is prepared to be frank." She paused for a moment and her soft lips set unnaturally hard. "I meant what I said, Stella. I don't intend to let you break up my marriage."

She did mean it. The determination had been born complete and firm immediately she realised what Stella was and understood at last how wrong the Dermot family had been about the beautiful girl they called their dark star.

Dark star!

It had a new and ominous meaning now. Odd that the old woman had been so right. But, as Stella herself had said, forewarned was forearmed, and the old cliché was quite right. She intended to fight for her marriage, using every weapon in her possession and with very few scruples if need be. Stella herself would have no hesitation in dispensing with scruples. She had already shown that.

In her new understanding of Stella, she became convinced that, even if her sister had used her charm and beauty to such good effect that she made Ruiz infatuated with her, she would never have agreed to a divorce, because Stella would never be able to make him happy. It would have been far better to suffer any amount of cold dislike from him and unhappiness for herself, rather than allow him to be disillusioned yet again, because any man who loved Stella would ultimately know her for what she was.

Stella had not yet had a chance to do much damage and so that was one thing to her advantage. One attraction had to die before another could take its place. Even if it was only physical attraction that Ruiz felt for her, Leigh knew that she was making him happy.

In her new understanding of Stella, she knew that her sister could never really love any man. If she did try to take Ruiz away—and it seemed that she had already started to try to do so—then it would only be a desire for his money and position, probably also a desire for him to make love to her, because Ruiz was, after all, a man who attracted women, but it could only be physical attraction, because Stella, she knew now, was a girl who could neither give nor inspire real love, and if the fight was to take place on that level, then Leigh considered that she had every right to protect her marriage and the man she loved. If Stella had been somebody else, somebody of a different type altogether, then it would not have been such a clear-cut decision, but when it was only an attraction of the senses and that was something his wife could give him, then that gave her a right to fight for him, because she loved him and she would do everything in her power to make him happy, while Stella would be thinking mainly of herself. If she had to fight Stella, then she would do it on her sister's own ground if necessary.

She was making Ruiz happy. Surely because of that she was entitled to fight for him? To fight to continue this happiness?

"Well?" Stella's voice broke into her thoughts. "What now? I suppose you'll want me to pack my bags and leave."

"That's rather obvious, I should imagine," Leigh said, still with the same quietness.

"And what will you tell Ruiz?" She laughed mockingly. "That you think your sister is trying to steal your rich husband?"

"His money doesn't mean anything to me."

Stella laughed again, but it still had that jibing derision. "You know, I almost believe you. You're one of those idiots who would fall in love with a man and not care if he didn't have a bean to his name." She turned towards the door, but stopped there and spoke almost airily. "You'd really better get used to the idea of making do with Bruce, because I intend to have Ruiz, you know."

"And I intend that you will not break up my marriage," Leigh replied, never raising her voice from its even quietness.

"You think you can fight me?"

Stella's tone was almost arrogant, so sure of her attraction, but Leigh's quietness did not change.

"I shall try. You can only use physical attraction, Stella. You've nothing else to give a man. If necessary, I'll fight you on your own ground. I'm not exactly a gorgon myself. Marriage to Ruiz has taught me that."

"Then I wish you luck," Stella mocked, and with a little wave of her hand she went out.

Leigh stood there with the coldness slowly creeping over her. In spite of what she had said, she was afraid. Stella was so beautiful and so completely unscrupulous. Perhaps she would succeed in the end. Ruiz was after all a man, with quite normal emotions.

"We of Mexico have Spanish blood and perhaps, as the world claims, we are more easily roused to emotions than others," she remembered his voice saying.

That was how Stella would work, of course.

"Whew!" Bruce whistled softly. "I didn't know you had it in you, Leigh." He shook his head suddenly and caught her wrists. "You can't win, though. Not against Stella."

"I can try."

"But it isn't worth it." He tightened his hold on her wrists and attempted to draw her nearer. "Let her have him. We were happy together once. We could be again."

Leigh shook him off almost absently. "That's all over and done with."

"It needn't be. And it might be the best way," he urged. "Stella's unscrupulous," he added, echoing her own thoughts. "She'll find some way to win in the end. If you came back with me now you could save yourself a lot of unhappiness."

"I won't let her win. I'll find some way to stop her. I have to . . . because I love Ruiz. She'll only make him unhappy, if she does win."

Bruce's face abruptly darkened and his grip on her arms became almost painful. With a quick movement he shifted his hold and drew her completely into his arms, her indifference to him suddenly inflaming him.

"You can't love him!" he muttered as she struggled with him. "You love me. You said you only married him because of Stella." He bent his head, his sullen anger growing as she tried to avoid him. "I'll prove it to you."

Leigh tried to turn her head away, but he was too strong for her and in that moment, if anything had been needed to prove how completely she had recovered from her infatuation from him, she had proof. She found his kiss actually repugnant.

Meantime, out in the hall, Stella had paused. The front door had just opened and the tall, dark figure of her sister's husband entered. He inclined his head slightly.

"*Buenos tardes*, Stella."

The deceptively sweet and charming smile curved her lips as she returned his greeting, but as he closed the door and came farther into the hall she moved quickly, pretending she thought he had been about to go into the room at the left, from which she had just emerged.

"Please don't go in there."

He stopped, his eyes narrowing as he looked down at her. "Why not?" He spoke in clipped, terse English this time.

"Because Bruce is in there . . . with Leigh."

This time he did move towards the door, sharply, almost involuntarily, but she caught his arm.

"Please—you mustn't be angry. I told you before you went away . . ." He had stopped at her quick, restraining hand on his arm and now she allowed a little pause. "Did you think about what I said?"

"Yes." He turned back to her, fully—and he suddenly shook her hand off his arm as if it had been something poisonous to the touch. "But you will allow my wife and me to work out our own lives. And another thing—you will please make some excuse to leave my house. We have a tradition of Spanish hospitality, but this time I must break it. I do not wish to have to tell my wife that her sister is a cheating, lying and completely heartless woman who is doing her best to spoil her life, as she once tried to do in England, merely for diversion."

"I don't..." Stella began, but he interrupted her quite sharply.

"I think you do understand. And another thing—this Bruce Jermyn. I do not know if you have arranged this thing between you, but you will understand also that I will not under any circumstances allow my wife to return to him. You requested that I think about what you told me and I have done so. I do not believe she loves him and in any case I would never let her go to a man who had once left her for a woman such as you. And now you will please make arrangements to leave."

With that he inclined his head in a short little salute and went into the room she had stopped him entering a few minutes ago. Stella, for once completely nonplussed, stood there for a moment, then her face slowly darkened with fury. She bit out an expletive that would have surprised many people who thought they knew her—and merely caused contemptuous amusement in those who really did know her—and turned and ran up the stairs.

Ruiz closed the door behind him and stood there for a moment, his dark face completely devoid of expression. He could not have chosen a less opportune moment to enter and even though she knew she had lost, before the battle had even really commenced, if Stella could have witnessed that moment she would have felt malicious satisfaction—because at the instant that Ruiz entered, Bruce was kissing Leigh. Her satisfaction would not have lasted for long, though, because Leigh was quite obviously unwilling, and the instant she managed to get one hand free she bunched it into a fist and drove it furiously into his stomach. Bruce doubled up with a gasp and Ruiz's voice remarked amusedly:

"You are most unexpected, *querida.* It is the usual thing to box the ears."

Both of them swung round, Leigh paling and Bruce looking flustered, embarrassed and apprehensive at the same time. Ruiz bowed slightly, with the faintest touch of mocking amusement.

"*Buenos tardes,*" he said calmly. "I do not believe we have met before, but I think introductions are unnecessary."

"I... I—I can explain—"

"You mean you are just leaving? It is a pity that our

acquaintance is to be so short, but we shall excuse your understandably abrupt departure." He bowed suavely. "*Adios.*"

Bruce swung round with a choked sound and almost ran out of the room. Ruiz looked after him with a faintly amused expression on his dark, handsome face.

"For an Aldoret I am remarkably controlled," he commented almost musingly. "It must be the English blood I have inherited, I think."

"Ruiz . . ." Leigh started towards him, one hand held out, but came to a stop, not knowing how to go on. After the mischief that Stella had already caused, how could she explain the fact of him coming into the room to find another man kissing his wife—and, moreover, the man she had once been engaged to marry?

Ruiz smiled suddenly, the brilliant smile that always lit up his dark face.

"No explanations or excuses are necessary, *querida.*" He caught her hand and drew her nearer to him. "Did he really think that I would allow you to go away with him?"

Leigh gripped his arms with urgent hands. "Ruiz, I don't want to go with him. You've got to believe me. I don't know what Stella told you, but it was probably all lies."

"I do believe you—but I do not think I would have allowed you to go, even had you wanted to."

Leigh felt a thrill of pure happiness go through her. Stella and her mischief-making faded as if she had never existed.

"Why?" she whispered, but instinct and the months of happiness they had already had together had already told her the answer.

"Because a man does not give up the woman he loves, not without a fight."

The next moment she was in his arms and their kiss was a mutual expression of complete love and trust in each other. Leigh knew then that she had never really had anything to fear from Stella, because those months together had built up something that could never be destroyed.

After a moment Ruiz held her away from him, looking down into her face with warm dark eyes and, in the manner of all men, wanting to know just when his beloved had first considered him to be above all other men.

Leigh smiled. "Oh, for ages and ages," she told him, "but I don't think I quite realised what was happening to me until you asked me to give you an heir for Carastrano, then I discovered that all my arguments about you evading the terms of the will really came from a subconscious desire that our marriage was a real one. I'd just been fooling myself with all that talk about Carastrano."

He laughed softly, in what appeared to be complete satisfaction. "And I think that I too had been fooling myself. Even then I must have wanted you as my wife for always."

"You said then that you did not believe in love."

"I was a fool. A man who does not love is only half alive."

"And a woman too," she agreed softly.

The dark eyes smiled into hers. "Then we agree that we are both very much alive." The smile died and he suddenly looked very serious. "You spoke a moment ago of your sister. There is something you wish to say about her?"

Leigh dropped her glance. "No, not now." Now that Stella was no longer in a position to cause trouble, she could afford to be generous. There was no need for Ruiz to know the truth about her sister, and how much she, personally, had overheard.

Ruiz's long, strong fingers caught her chin and turned her head, so that she had to face him. He looked at her searchingly for a moment, then nodded.

"I think that you have at last learned what she is really like."

Leigh's lips parted in amazement. "Ruiz, you knew . . . ?"

"I have always known," he said quietly. "And now I do not think that it will hurt you to learn that I have asked her to leave."

Leigh laughed suddenly. "*You* asked her to leave! I'd already given her her walking orders."

He smiled at that. "It is good that we think so much alike."

Very much alike, Leigh thought to herself in happy satisfaction. She had been quite prepared to fight Stella, on whatever grounds her sister chose, and it seemed that Ruiz had come back from Carastrano equally determined not to let their marriage be broken. But in that case, why had he gone away as he had?

"But if you always knew what Stella was like, that she was deliberately trying to make mischief," she asked aloud, "why did you go away to Carastrano like that? It *was* because of something she said, wasn't it?"

He nodded. "Yes, because I knew there was a certain amount of truth in her words, however much she might have been twisting them to suit her own purposes." He paused, frowning slightly. "When you married me you were in love with this . . . this Bruce Jermyn." That was said with the suggestion of a scowl, but it turned to a smile when she put up a hand and gently smoothed it out. He caught her hand, pressing a kiss into the soft palm. "I had persuaded you to make our marriage a real one and you seemed to be happy," he continued, "but then your sister came. She told me that Bruce still loved you, that he knew it was only a business marriage—or had been—and that he had come to Mexico to try to take you back with him, but that you had sent him away because of some mistaken loyalty to me. There seemed much possible truth in that," his slight accent becoming somewhat more pronounced there. "And I discovered in that moment how much I had been fooling myself. It was not just a case of mental compatibility and a certain amount of physical attraction. I was in love with you—and faced suddenly with the thought of perhaps having to give you up. You seemed to be happy with me, but I did not know if underneath you were still longing for this man in England. So I went back to Carastrano, to try to come to some decision. But there was no need to seek for truth at Carastrano. It was all around me. Memories of our happiness there. I knew that we could not have been so happy if we were not both in love. It needed only one night there to tell me that. Perhaps you had not yet realised it, but I was sure of it and I came back intending to refuse to give you your freedom if you should ask me for it. I was so certain that I was prepared to face unhappiness for a while, until you realised that you belonged to me and the other was only the lingering remnants of old habit, thinking yourself in love with him."

She laughed suddenly. "Habit! Like an old boot that somebody had forgotten to throw out." How chagrined Bruce would be at such a description. "But there wasn't even habit," she said. "I didn't feel a thing, except irritation that he was making a nuisance of himself ... and then fear, when I knew what Stella was really like ... and what she was trying to do." She paused, shaking her head curiously. "Isn't it strange that we should have both had the same idea? You prepared to put up with me hating you for a while when you refused to let me go to Bruce, and me feeling the same way about Stella."

"Not really strange," he said quietly. "We both knew that we belonged to each other and we believed it so firmly we were prepared to undergo anything for it. Perhaps in a way she had to come here, so that we should know how much we meant to each other." He drew her closely into his arms again. "And now we shall forget about her. Soon she will be gone from here and we shall go back to Carastrano together."

Back to Carastrano, back to complete and lasting happiness. She smiled up at him, knowing that their marriage, which had started so strangely, crossing strange seas, had at last reached the harbour that everyone sought.

The dark star had set.

OTHER HARLEQUIN ROMANCES YOU MAY ENJOY . . .

☐ 1044 PARADISE ISLAND by Hilary Wilde

Lauren did not foresee all the difficulties that would arise when she was persuaded to masquerade as Nick Natal's wife and professional dancing partner because his real wife Natalie was too ill to accompany him to tropical Paradise Island.

☐ 1045 GREEN GIRL by Sara Seale

Harriet Jones, an eighteen-year-old orphan, thought she had met her Prince Charming when Rory Lonnegan asked her to come to Ireland to marry him. But a disappointment was in store for Harriet when she arrived at Castle Clooney.

☐ 1057 LESLEY BOWEN M.D. by Marjorie Norrell

Lesley was blessed with exceptional beauty. But was it such a blessing, when it meant that although she only wanted to become a good doctor, few people would take her seriously — while the woman-hating Doctor Mark Crossman seemed actively to resent her ?

☐ 1058 NURSE AT ROWANBANK by Flora Kidd

Margaret Dunne went to Rowanbank as a private nurse to pull herself out of the doldrums, and all was well, except for the insufferable Richard Morrell, who greeted her with the words "Plain, wholesome and oh, so good for us !"

☐ 1061 MEET ME IN ISTANBUL by Pamela Kent

Gay was living in Istanbul amid every kind of luxury — and yet she wanted to get away from it ! She felt that she was in a trap, though a silk-lined trap, and she must escape at all costs.
She appealed for help to Charles Villiers and that launched her into a series of extraordinary adventures.

☐ 1065 STUDENT NURSE AT SWALE by Pauline Ash

As Sister Tutor surveyed the newest bunch of recruits to the Preleminary Training School, she decided that one of them a least, Saskia Lawrence — Sandy to her friends — was no ordinary little student nurse. And how right she was !

All books are 60¢ each, check titles required and mail page with order coupon.